THE EDUCATION OF THE OSTEOPATHIC PHYSICIAN

Rochelle P. Gershenow
Editor

Published by:
American Association of Colleges of Osteopathic Medicine

International Standard Book Number: 0-918843-00-6

Acknowledgements

Sincere appreciation is extended to those people without whose efforts and input this book would never have come to fruition.

Anthony J. McNevin, CAE, Executive Director of the American Association of Colleges of Osteopathic Medicine (AACOM), whose interest and perseverance made the project possible. Mr. Jordan Braverman, who authored much of the book. Members of AACOM's Section of Student Affairs Officers who provided input, in particular, Dr. Michael Budd, Dr. Harold Hakes, and Dr. Darrell Rishel who planned the format and reviewed the material. The executive committee of AACOM's Board of Governors, Dr. George Northup, and Dr. Philip Greenman, all of whom reviewed the book. And many other persons, too numerous to name, who also provided input to the final edition of this book.

Rochelle P. Gershenow
Editor

Preface

*O*ne of the fastest growing fields in America today is that of health care. As the demand for medical care services continues to grow, the need for a variety of health professionals is not expected to lessen in future years. One profession which will require increasing manpower is that of osteopathic medicine. More than 100 years old, osteopathic medicine is playing a very important role in providing comprehensive family health services to those in need and in geographic areas of the country where the need is very great.

As your school's pre-medical advisor, you can assume an important role in bringing to the attention of your students the opportunities which are available in osteopathic medicine. Consequently, this book has been prepared as an educational service with you and your students in mind. The book begins with a discussion of the history and philosophy of osteopathic medicine. It details the kind of medical education which osteopathic medicine requires, the schools which provide it as well as internship, residency, and licensure requirements. It examines the various practice options available to osteopathic physicians as well as the kinds of professional osteopathic organizations which exist to assist the physician in his/her professional career. In addition, the book contains a listing of osteopathic medical schools — their requirements for admission as well as matriculation. Should your students desire additional information, they may contact the school(s) of interest. It is hoped that the information presented herein will enable you and your students to gain an understanding of osteopathic medicine and will assist you in helping your students determine their career choice.

Table of Contents

Introduction

American health care is undergoing a revolution. As our population increases and scientific medical breakthroughs rapidly accelerate, adding years to our life, the cost and demand for medical care keep rising. To meet this situation, new health care delivery and payment systems have evolved in recent years and the demand for medical personnel to provide health services continues to grow. One professional who has had and still has a very important role in our health care delivery system is the osteopathic physician. Doctors of Osteopathy (D.O.) are not chiropractors, bone specialists or physical therapists. They are physicians: Like Doctors of Medicine (M.D.), they are fully licensed to provide comprehensive medical care. They use scientifically accepted methods of diagnosis and treatment. Like their M.D. counterpart, they work in hospitals, clinics, private offices and other health care settings.

Osteopathic medicine has a basic underlying philosophy. It views the human body as a unit. All body systems, including the musculoskeletal system, are inter-related and function together both in health and disease. This is sometimes referred to as a "whole-istic" approach. In addition to using all the tools of modern medicine to detect and treat disease, osteopathic physicians do more. They are specifically trained to perform osteopathic manipulation. This is a technique in which osteopathic physicians use their hands to aid in the diagnosis of illness and is part of the total treatment of patients. They pay particular attention to the musculoskeletal system. As a result of manipulation, circulation can be improved and the normalization of the blood and nerve supply can help the body heal itself. But unlike the Doctor of Medicine, neither the Doctor of Osteopathy nor his field of practice is as well known to the general public or the student who is considering a career in medicine.

History

Osteopathic medicine is more than 100 years old. It traces its origins in the United States to the Civil War period when a young allopathic physician, Andrew Taylor Still (1828-1917) founded this new medical discipline. A Civil War soldier, abolitionist, suffragist, and son of a missionary doctor, Dr. Still objected to the prevailing medical practices of the day, on the grounds that they were mostly ineffectual and even dangerous. At the time, physicians used such treatment methods as leeches, bloodletting, and purges as well as obscure drug recipes. In 1874, Dr. Still formulated a philosophy of medicine called osteopathy. This concept is based upon establishing proper body mechanics and stimulating various organ systems in order to restore health. Dr. Still believed that Man should be studied as a total unit. He believed that within the human body were substances which were necessary for the maintenance of health, and if properly stimulated, these substances also might be necessary to contribute to the cure of some diseases. He did not believe that disease was strictly an outside agent inflicting evil on the body, but rather was a normal response to an abnormal body situation. In his search for the positive quality of health, Dr. Still discovered, as others had noted throughout history, that the skeleton and its supporting muscles and ligaments were subject to certain mechanical laws, and therefore, were the objects of stresses and strains. He observed through careful study that when joints, restricted in motion due to mechanical locking or other related causes, were normalized, certain body dysfunctions improved. Through experiments and clinical observations, Dr. Still refined the art of manipulative treatment, applied directly to the musculoskeletal system. This "hands on treatment" was also used centuries ago by Hippocrates, the "father" of modern medicine.

While continuing to use most of the medical and surgical armamentarium of the day in his medical practice, Dr. Still talked to anyone who would listen about his new philosophy. More specifically, as a result of many years of study, he evolved the following principles:

The body is an integral unit, a whole. The structure of the body and its functions work together interdependently.

The body systems have built-in repair processes which are self-regulating and self-healing in the face of disease.

The circulatory system or distributing channels of the body, along with the nervous system, provide the integrating functions for the rest of the body. Their free and unimpeded flow carries both the maintenance and repair capabilities of the body.

The contribution of the musculoskeletal system to a person's health is much more than providing framework and support. It is one of the most vulnerable considerations in response to stress. Improper musculoskeletal functioning can impede essential blood and nerve supply.

While disease may be manifested in specific parts of the body, other parts may contribute to a restoration or correction of the disease.

A. T. Still.

In due course, word of Dr. Still's reputation began to spread and sufferers began to come in great numbers to Kirksville, Missouri, where he had settled. Because he needed help with numerous patients and believed firmly that his practice was a philosophy that could be taught, Dr. Still founded, in Kirksville, the American School of Osteopathy in 1892. Osteopathic medicine soon became the target of attack by organized allopathic medicine and individual Doctors of Medicine. Despite these attacks, the osteopathic medical profession began to grow. By 1897, it was felt that a national organization was needed. Thus, the American Association for the Advancement of Osteopathy (whose name changed to the American Osteopathic Association in 1901) was founded. A few months later in 1897, the Associated Colleges of Osteopathy (now the American Association of Colleges of Osteopathic Medicine) was formed.

But in Dr. Still's lifetime the controversy continued, much of it focusing on his eccentric personality and outspoken views. His fervent espousal of osteopathic methods was interpreted by others as a rejection of all other medical treatments. Dr. Still's rejection of other medical methods was a *selective* one, and he did not hold osteopathic manipulation to be the only acceptable form of treatment. Rather than becoming discouraged by the attacks, Dr. Still became even more convinced of the validity of his philosophy and additional form of treatment. When Dr. Still died in 1917, there were 5,000 osteopathic physicians in the country. As of August 1984, the American Osteopathic Association reported that there were 22,746 physicians in this medical field.

Historically, osteopathic physicians have had to struggle for their professional recognition and independence at every step. In many states, they were obliged to accept regulation by the M.D. establishment. Early licensing by states did not allow the Doctor of Osteopathy to prescribe drugs or perform surgery despite the fact that these skills were taught in osteopathic medical colleges. Thus, their medical practice in some states was limited to distinctively osteopathic manipulative therapy. The practical effect of the laws limiting their practice was to reduce them to something akin to physical therapists. The public might go to a Doctor of Medicine (M.D.) for one kind of medical service, and to a Doctor of Osteopathy (D.O.) for another. For D.O.s, second rate status was conferred by legislation in some states, although the status was not an objective fact. The change to full licensure was gradual. One landmark in this process was a court decision in Audrian County, Missouri, in 1950 which established the right of D.O.s to practice as complete physicians and surgeons

Left: A. T. Still, Founder of Osteopathic Medicine.

Below: First School of Osteopathy and birthplace cabin of A. T. Still.

in a county hospital. The court defined the practice of osteopathic medicine to include prescribing or administering drugs and performing surgery with instruments. After 1950, a number of other legislative and regulatory bodies moved to provide full practice rights in their own jurisdictions. The last state granted full practice rights in 1973. Now osteopathic physicians (D.O.s) are licensed to practice the full scope of medicine in all 50 states and the District of Columbia.

Other improvements also developed such as the field of osteopathic medical education. At the turn of the century, in 1902, the American Association of Colleges of Osteopathic Medicine developed standards for college approval. The American Osteopathic Association began to inspect the colleges in 1903, and the American Association of Colleges of Osteopathic Medicine took on the formal role of approving schools. Meanwhile in 1904, the osteopathic medical profession adopted a code of ethics. In 1952, the American Osteopathic Association was recognized by the U.S. Office of Education for the purpose of accrediting osteopathic medical colleges. In 1967, the American Osteopathic Association was recognized by the National Commission on Accrediting (now the Council on Postsecondary Accreditation) as the accrediting agency for all facets of osteopathic medical education.

The number of osteopathic medical colleges in the country was also undergoing change. By 1900, there were eleven more colleges of osteopathic medicine established — in Philadelphia; Des Moines; Chicago; Wilkes-Barre; Denver; Boston; San Francisco; Milwaukee; Minneapolis; Fargo; and Franklin, Kentucky — in addition to the one established by Dr. Still at Kirksville. By the mid-1920s, mergers among a number of schools in various geographic areas had left only seven; one more closed in the 1940s, leaving six, and one of these (The College of Osteopathic Physicians and Surgeons in Los Angeles) was converted to an allopathic medical school in California in 1962, leaving five: Chicago, Des Moines, Kansas City, Kirksville, and Philadelphia. The recent growth in educational institutions began in 1966 when the charter was obtained for the Texas College of Osteopathic Medicine. The founding of other schools followed in rapid succession: Michigan State University College of Osteopathic Medicine (1969) — the first college of osteopathic medicine to be housed in a university, West Virginia School of Osteopathic Medicine (1972), The Oklahoma College of Osteopathic Medicine and Surgery (1972), Ohio University College of Osteopathic Medicine (1975), University of Medicine and Dentistry of New Jersey — School of Osteopathic Medicine (1976), New York College of Osteopathic Medicine of New York Institute of Technology (1976), College of Osteopathic Medicine of the Pacific (1977), University of New England College of Osteopathic Medicine (1978), and Southeastern College of Osteopathic Medicine (1979), making 15 schools in all. Other sites and organizations for new schools continue to be discussed.

As the profession continued to develop, osteopathic hospitals were established, new training programs begun, and, in 1934, the American Osteopathic Hospital Association was founded. The first inspection and approval of osteopathic hospitals for the training of interns took place in 1936. The Advisory Board of Osteopathic Specialists and first specialty board (Radiology) came into existence in 1939. In 1944, standards for osteopathic hospitals not involved in training of interns were adopted, and a registry of hospitals meeting these standards was published in 1945. In 1947, the first residency training programs were approved even though residencies existed in osteopathic hospitals prior to that time.

Today, the osteopathic medical profession continues to progress. The federal government recognizes D.O.s and M.D.s as being equals. This means that all important federal medical programs are open to both professions: funding for research and hospitals' construction, Medicare and Medicaid, financial assistance to osteopathic and allopathic medical students, and service as medical officers in the Public Health Service and the armed forces. D.O.s and M.D.s work together in numerous joint staff hospitals, and this number continues to increase; moreover, any hospital receiving federal assistance risks court action should it attempt to deny privileges to osteopathic physicians. At present, D.O.s serve the largest and smallest communities of America. More than 16 percent are found in communities of 500,000 or more, and about 54 percent are active in areas of under 50,000 population. Thus, two of every three osteopathic physicians are serving in areas of the nation's greatest medical needs. The gains made by osteopathic physicians in recent years are largely due to their commitment to family and community medicine. Many of those sectors not served by allopathic medicine (especially rural and small town areas) have been served by family doctors in the osteopathic tradition. With the increasing demand for medical care not likely to wane in the future as our nation's population increases and grows older, the role of osteopathic physicians in our health care delivery system also increases.

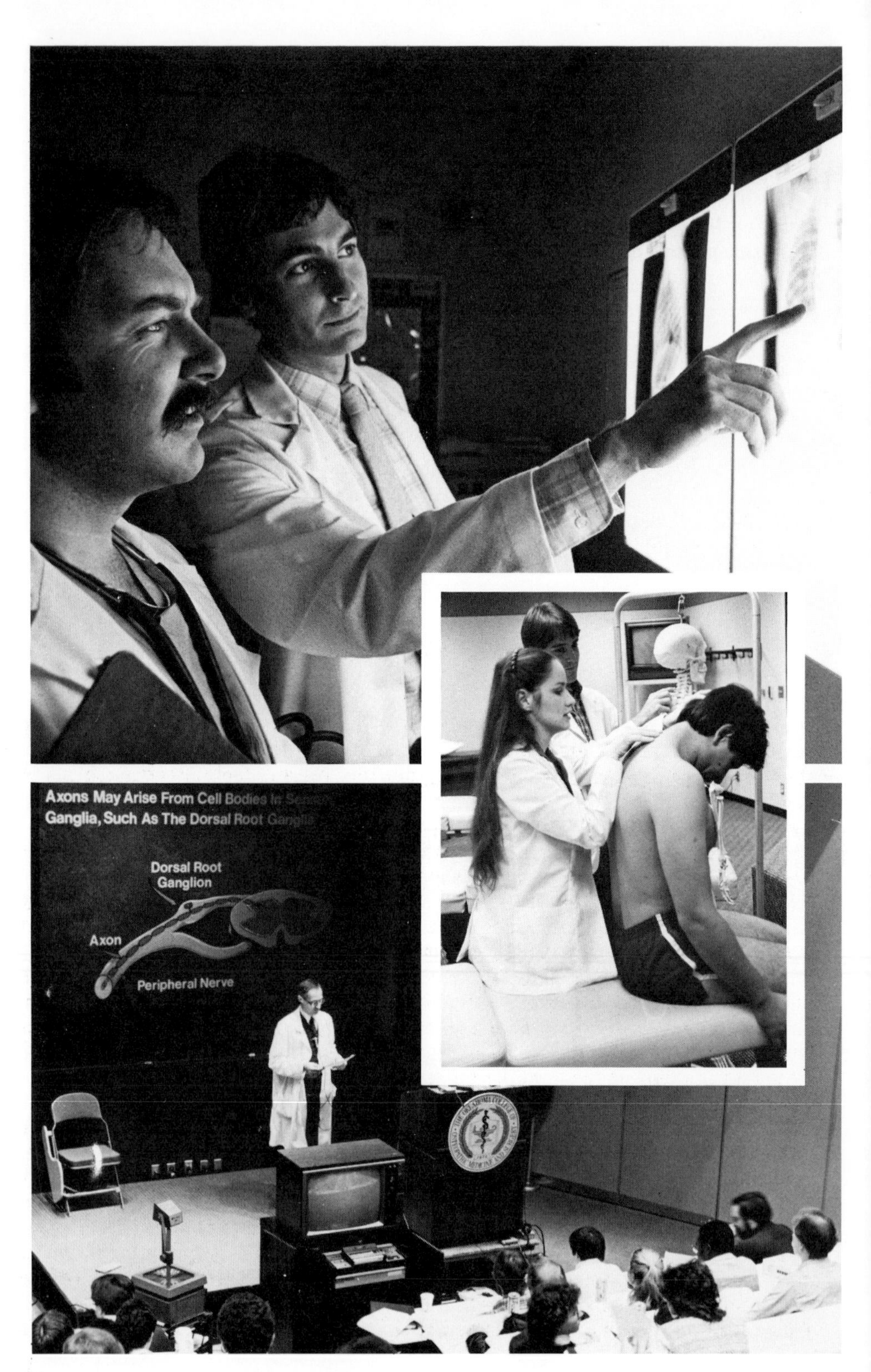
Axons May Arise From Cell Bodies In
Ganglia, Such As The Dorsal Root
Dorsal Root
Ganglion
Axon
Peripheral Nerve

Philosophy of Osteopathic Medicine

The word osteopathy is derived from the Greek "osteo" meaning bone and "pathos" meaning to suffer or to be in sympathy with. When Dr. Andrew Taylor Still formulated this new medical philosophy, its emphasis on the musculoskeletal components of the human body gave rise to its name.

In formulating a method of manual medicine for patient treatment, Dr. Still borrowed from a 4,000 year old legacy which included application of massage and manipulation. The oldest recorded writings on manual medicine mention the use of massage in China. About 2700 B.C., massage was popular in Greek and Roman life and became an integral part of early medical care. In relatively more recent times, seventeenth century physicians reported strong competition from itinerant bonesetters who reputedly brought about cures through manipulation. But it was not until 1813 — about 60 years before Dr. Still began to espouse osteopathy — that manual medicine was recognized as being therapeutic. In Sweden, Henrik Ling developed and practiced a system of massage that he called Kinestherapy. In Bonn, Dr. Johann Metzger instructed physicians in the techniques of clinical massage and was known throughout the world for the results he was able to achieve.

But osteopathic medicine was to be more than simple massage or manipulation. The osteopathic physician would continue to use traditional diagnostic and treatment methods. But, in addition, he would palpate the body to determine the character of its skin, musculature, and bones. The range and quality of joint motion would be evaluated both by passive and active motion. Where appropriate, the physician would then design and apply manipulative treatment. This added a new dimension to the practice of medicine.

In addition to the use of osteopathic manipulative treatment, the osteopathic physician has been trained to remember that the disease or structure being treated is only part of the total person. This approach means that the osteopathic physician sees the patient as a whole person and becomes involved not just with the disease and list of symptoms, but is concerned with the total patient. Thus, there is a genuine concern about the interrelationship of the patient's health, work, home, and family. Also, the osteopathic physician understands that there is a need for patient education so that the patient can achieve and maintain good health. This combination of traditional medicine, osteopathic evaluation, manipulation, and concern for the patient forms the rational therapy which Dr. Still announced more than 100 years ago.

Functional Principles of the Human Body

In diagnosing and treating patients, osteopathic physicians are guided by certain general principles concerning the normal functioning of the human body.

The first of these principles is that the human body is a unit; it is an integrated organism in which no part works independently. An abnormal structure or function in one part of the body may exert unfavorable influences on other parts, and therefore, on the body as a whole. This view, generally attributed to Hippocrates, the "father of medicine," recognizes that the body is not just a network of independent compartments. It is not simply a human machine comprised of a heart, lungs, intestines, and other organs. It is instead a complexly interrelated community of organs and systems — the cardiovascular system, the gastrointestinal system, the neurological system, and the circulatory system among others — each dependent and interwoven in its structure and function with others, each compensating with the other to meet the constant demands of internal and external stress. Diseases of internal organs affect the structural components of the body. Likewise, problems in the neuro-muscular system of the body can affect the internal organs. Dr. Still believed that any rational therapy would be responsive to these factors. For hundreds of years, physicians had treated diseases by concentrating on separate organs in the body. They had avoided consideration and treatment of the musculoskeletal system which makes up more than 60 percent of the body. Dr. Still's new rational medicine added treatment of this system to his predecessors' sole use of pharmacy and surgery. Thus, the osteopathic physician recognizes that while a specific organ may become the central focus of an illness, the effects of the illness are felt in varying degrees throughout the body. Only when the whole body has returned to its normal balance has the alleviation of the illness been truly achieved.

The second principle states that the body, through a complex system of internal checks and balances, tends to be self-regulating and self-healing in the face of stress and disease. Today, the modern science of immunology supports Dr. Still's view that the body has a self-protecting mechanism. It's now called the immune system. Self-regulation of the body is explained by the modern concepts of nerve reflex function and endocrinology. Osteopathic physicians, through their knowledge of physiology, recognize that health and illness are not separate, distinct, and diametrically opposite conditions. The body, rather than resting in a state of health or illness, is constantly fluctuating between the two. It is engaged in a never-ending struggle to adapt itself to the ever changing demands of its internal and external environment. It seeks through constant change to resist, neutralize, and overcome the continual stresses, physical and psychic, to which it is subjected. The body's ability to fluctuate and adapt to stress determines the degree or state of its health. If it can meet the various forms of stress, adequately and without exaggeration, it will remain healthy. But when some disorder within the body disrupts its adaptability, or when some force in the external environment overwhelms the checks and balances of internal equilibrium, disease and illness take the upper hand. Illness, despite the countless stresses to which the body is subjected, is for most people only an occasional experience. It must follow, therefore, that in most instances, the body is able to resist disease and overcome illness without our being consciously aware of the drama that is occurring.

The third principle states that adequate function of all body organs and systems depends upon the integrating forces of the nervous and circulatory systems. In order to function normally, the organs and systems must be constantly controlled by nerve impulses. Nerve impulses transmitted to and from the brain and spinal cord not only excite or inhibit the actions of individual organs and tissues but cause them, in effect, to lose their individuality and become interacting and interdependent parts of a cooperative enterprise. Blood transported via the circulatory system brings food and oxygen to all cells of the body and removes their waste products. Blood, however, is more than a means of transportation. In its journey through the body, blood connects and integrates the function of one part of the body with the others — the lungs with the intestines with the liver with the muscles — so that the entire body can function and respond as a whole.

Remembering the first principle of body unity, it becomes clear that any disturbance in the circulatory or nervous systems must, in some degree, affect the function of the body as a whole.

In summary, we have noted that the human body is an integrated organism with an inherent capacity to resist disease and heal itself. Health and illness are conditions of the whole organism. Abnormal structure or function in one part of the body exerts abnormal influences on other parts and on the body as a whole. The nervous and circulatory systems, finally, not only integrate the normal functions of the body, but if disturbed, inhibit the body's natural resistive and reparative powers.

Osteopathic and Allopathic Medicine: The Distinction

In terms of a therapeutic practice philosophy, osteopathic physicians constantly keep in mind that the human body is an integrated organism with an inherent capacity to resist disease and heal itself. The allopathic physicians' philosophy emphasizes the value of the type of intervention used rather than the value of the steps necessary to increase the host's resistance.

The fundamental contribution of the osteopathic medical profession, based upon the previous principles, is the recognition that the body's musculoskeletal system (bones, joints, connective tissues, skeletal muscles, and tendons) plays an important role in the body's continuous effort to resist and overcome illness and disease. Osteopathic physicians have repeatedly demonstrated that this largest of body systems both reflects internal illness and may actually aggravate or accelerate the process of disease. Based on this recognition, the osteopathic profession has developed a unique system of diagnosis and treatment that, alone or when employed in conjunction with other standard medical procedures, is highly beneficial in the treatment and prevention of disease.

The distinctive feature which separates osteopathic medicine from allopathic medicine (M.D.) is manipulative treatment or "biomechanics" as it has begun to be called. This form of therapy is an additional component to osteopathic education, and is largely absent from allopathic medical education. The allopathic physicians only learn about the musculoskeletal system in a traditional orthopedic sense (treatment of sprains, strains, fractures, dystrophics, etc.). Osteopathic manipulative treatment differs from the manual techniques practiced by chiropractors and others in significant ways. Osteopathic manipulative treatment is not limited to correcting "subluxations" of the spine nor is it limited to correcting disorders of the musculoskeletal system. For example, it has proven effective as part of a treatment program for organic diseases such as asthma, by freeing the restricted movement of the rib cage and allowing unimpaired ventilation. In osteopathic practices, manipulative treatment is an *additional* method, used along with all the standard diagnostic and therapeutic techniques such as X-ray examinations, drug prescriptions, and surgery of all kinds. In comparison to Dr. Still's time, osteopathic manipulative treatment as such, occupies a much smaller segment of the osteopathic physician's total range of skills and knowledge — for medical science has expanded enormously in recent decades and Doctors of Osteopathy have drawn upon its advances.

Differences Between D.O.s and M.D.s

However, these latter points raise another question. What are the basic differences between an allopathic physician (Doctor of Medicine) and an osteopathic physician (Doctor of Osteopathy). First, let us cite some similarities. Both are fully trained physicians who have taken a prescribed amount of premedical training, graduated from an undergraduate college and received four years of training in a medical school. The young osteopathic physician then takes a year's rotating internship in a hospital with an approved intern training program. If he or she elects to practice any one of a number of medical specialties, the physician then enters into a three- or four-year residency training program. Whether one becomes a Doctor of Medicine or Doctor of Osteopathy, the route of training is similar, but not synonymous. Both are alike in that they use scientifically accepted methods of diagnosis and treatment. They are also licensed by the same state medical boards; osteopathic physicians are licensed to practice in all phases of medicine in all 50 states of the country.

The basic difference between Doctors of Osteopathy and Doctors of Medicine is that the osteopathic profession has pioneered an emphasis on the disorders of the musculoskeletal system and has developed and used manipulative treatment, as already noted, with wide acceptance in treating such disorders. The emphasis on the relationship between the body structure and organic functioning gives a broader base for the treatment of the patient as a unit.

Another basic difference is the emphasis on specialization within allopathic and osteopathic medicine. While allopathic medicine has witnessed over time, an increase in the number of physicians who choose a specialty with the subsequent decline in the proportion of physicians choosing general practice, osteopathic medicine through its educational system has emphasized the training of family doctors. The osteopathic profession is known for supplying doctors to underserved medical areas where the doctor is truly a physician to the family, literally caring for the family from the cradle to the grave. While the practitioner certainly renders primary care (its components being general and family practice, internal medicine, pediatrics, and obstetrics/gynecology), he/she renders much more. The osteopathic physician becomes an integral part of the family life of those he/she serves.

The commitment of osteopathic medicine to family and community care is reflected in its curriculum. While allopathic medicine has gained prestige through the development of large medical research complexes and the selection of students who are also research oriented, osteopathic colleges have never conformed to this model. Clinical training most often occurs in community facilities (hospitals, clinics) and physicians' offices rather than in large metropolitan teaching hospitals. At every step of the way, there is reaffirmation and pride in the tradition of family practice. Although osteopathic physicians can earn certification in the same medical specialties as allopathic physicians, most osteopathic physicians choose family practice. By applying diagnostic and therapeutic methods and going beyond allopathic medicine in its distinctive recognition of the function of the musculoskeletal system in health and disease, osteopathic medicine provides a comprehensive and complete approach to man's health problems. While cooperating with all other branches of medicine, osteopathic medicine maintains its independence in order to develop and perpetuate for mankind this unique and inclusive system of medical care.

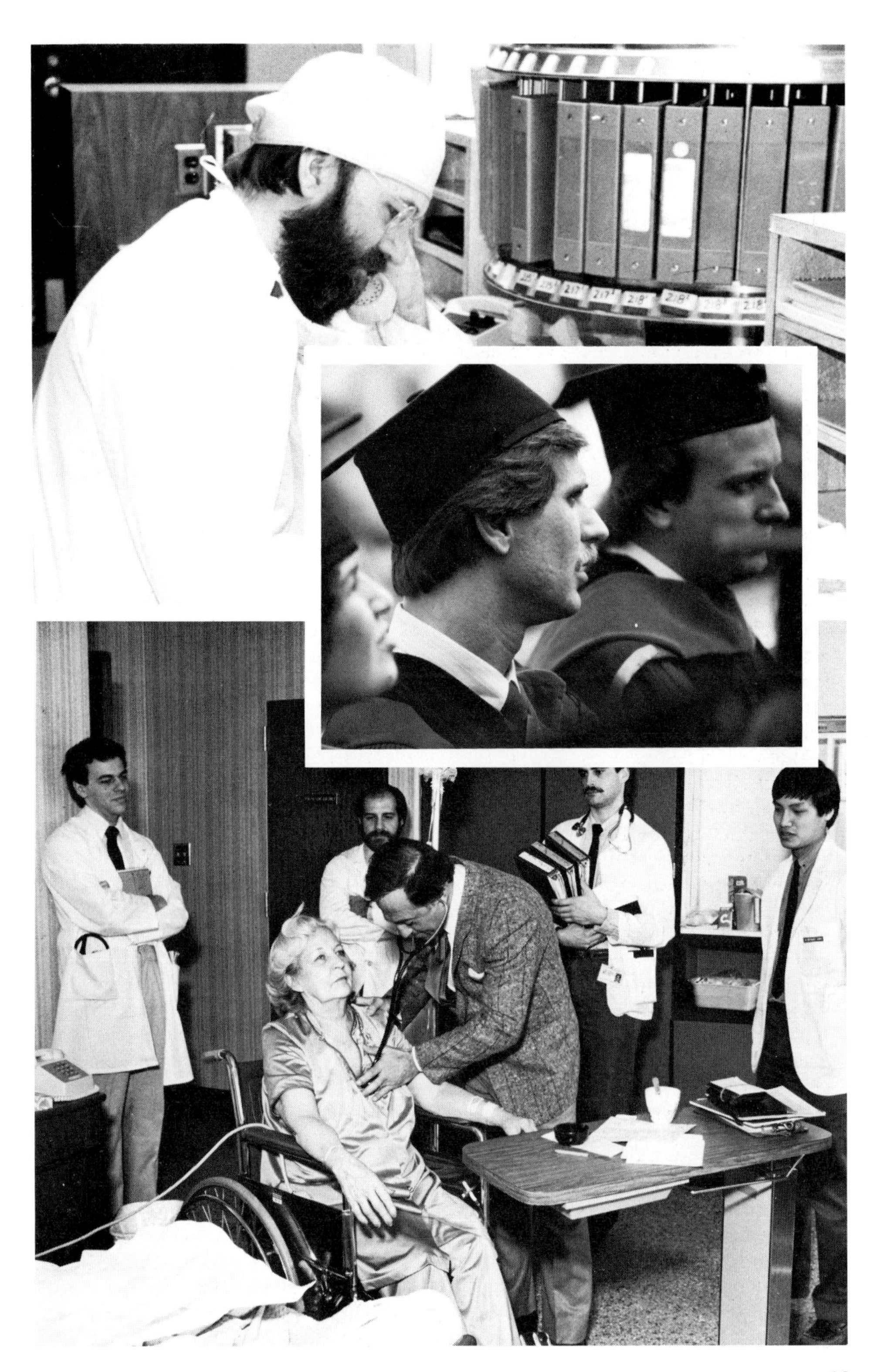

Osteopathic Education, Training and Licensure Requirements

It takes four years to complete the osteopathic medical program. Upon graduation students receive the Doctor of Osteopathy (D.O.) degree.

During the first two years in a college of osteopathic medicine, students receive basic science and pre-clinical instruction in a classroom and laboratory environment. Required subjects include anatomy, physiology, pathology, biochemistry, microbiology, and pharmacology. In addition, students may study nutrition, rehabilitation, geriatrics, and alcohol and drug abuse. In many instances, these subjects are included in basic or general courses. Most osteopathic medical colleges also provide instruction in the relationship between doctors and patients, occupational and environmental health, human sexuality, and the history of medicine. Each osteopathic medical college approaches its curriculum a little differently; organizing it by discipline or system. The traditional curriculum is structured by discipline. The systems curriculum incorporates basic and clinical sciences in the study of a major organ system. Some of the schools base their curriculum on a spiral approach. With this approach, study matter is continuously reintroduced to the student in greater depth and complexity, thus reinforcing prior learning and promoting meaningful retention.

After completing the basic science courses, students embark on a two-year period of clinical instruction which also may begin during their second year of study. Osteopathic clinical instruction is somewhat different than the allopathic model in that osteopathic experience is strongly community based. Rather than principally receiving instruction in large teaching hospitals as in allopathic medicine, osteopathic medical students are placed primarily in community hospitals, clinics, and physicians' offices. An osteopathic physician in the community may serve as the student's preceptor. Required subjects in the clinical years include general medicine, pediatrics, obstetrics/gynecology, surgery, radiology, and preventive medicine. In this phase of their instruction, students begin to assume their roles as physicians under the careful supervision of instructors who are themselves practicing physicians. They learn to recognize, diagnose, and treat a patient's symptoms and, for the first time, view the results of their training. This clinical instruction is often supplemented by lectures, clinical conferences, seminars, and other educational programs. Integrated throughout the osteopathic medical curriculum is instruction in osteopathic principles concerning the interrelationship of all body systems in health and disease, and training in osteopathic palpatory diagnosis and manipulation. Based on the "whole-istic" approach to individuals and their health problems, colleges of osteopathic medicine emphasize family, community, and preventive medicine.

Two other options to the traditional four-year course of study are also available in some of the osteopathic colleges. These include a combined D.O./M.S. program and a combined D.O./Ph.D. program which allow exceptional students to obtain both degrees in 4-6 years. This type of program is intended for the student with an interest in academic medicine who also possesses demonstrated research skills. The other option is an osteopathic fellowship program which is designed to expand the educational opportunities for students while they assist in all phases of the osteopathic principles and practices department's operation. The Fellows assist in lecturing, teaching of practical skills, and are encouraged to do research. Participation in the fellowship program extends the period of time necessary to complete the Doctor of Osteopathy degree from 4 to 5 years.

Internship

After receiving the Doctor of Osteopathy degree, the student serves a twelve month rotating internship at a hospital approved by the American Osteopathic Association. The new physician may also do an internship in a federal hospital. This graduate medical program is philosophically based on a broad generalist clinical curriculum which accounts for the relatively high percentage of osteopathic physicians engaging in general practice and/or the other primary care areas of internal medicine, pediatrics, and obstetrics/gynecology.

The intern rotates through specified clinical services of the hospital. Included are three months of internal medicine, three months of surgery, one month of general practice, one month of obstetrics and gynecology, and one month of pediatrics. The remaining three months are comprised of various rotations in anesthesiology, pathology, radiology, emergency medicine, and other medical services. In the osteopathic hospital, the intern is additionally trained in osteopathic principles and therapeutics.

This rotating internship offers the new physician a broad clinical experience emphasizing generalist skills and prepares him/her for entrance into general practice after completion of the internship. An internship enables the physician to gain a broad perspective of osteopathic medicine, thereby creating a firmer base upon which to make career choices. In addition, it prepares the physician for possible entrance into residency programs.

Residency Training

Upon completion of internship training, the osteopathic physician may choose to specialize in a particular medical field, or, subsequently, a subspecialty of that field. For example, internal medicine is a specialty whose subspecialties include cardiology, gastroenterology, allergy and immunology, oncology, endocrinology, or rheumatology to name but a few. Should an osteopathic physician choose to specialize, then a hospital residency in one of the specialty areas requires an additional one to six years of training. The number of years depends upon the specialty field and the standards established by the American Osteopathic Association and the particular specialty college so as to qualify for board certification. Osteopathic physicians can be board certified in the following specialty areas: Anesthesiology, Dermatology, Emergency Medicine, General Practice, Internal Medicine, Neurology and Psychiatry, Nuclear Medicine, Obstetrics and Gynecology, Ophthalmology and Otorhinolaryngology, Orthopedic Surgery, Osteopathic Manipulative Medicine, Pathology, Pediatrics, Proctology, Public Health and Preventive Medicine, Radiology, Rehabilitation Medicine, and Surgery. As of April 1, 1985, there were 5,871 Doctors of Osteopathy certified to practice medical specialties.

As far as nonosteopathic residencies are concerned, it is important to note that approval of a residency program in an allopathic medical institution would not be considered when there are approved programs in the same discipline within the osteopathic medical profession. However, when an osteopathic physician who has had an American Osteopathic Association approved internship is not able to obtain specialty training within the osteopathic field but can receive it in the allopathic profession, the individual may qualify for specialty approval by the American Osteopathic Association if he or she can present adequate documentation of the inability to obtain the training within the osteopathic community. Specialty training may also be obtained through Fellowships or preceptorships. In regard to the latter, an individual practicing osteopathic specialist may provide full- or part-time training in a designated field for a physician desiring such a preceptorship.

The osteopathic physician's studies do not end upon completion of his/her internship and/or residency. They last a lifetime. To ensure this being true, the American Osteopathic Association requires each practicing physician to complete a minimum number of hours of continuing medical education every three years during the life of his or her practice so that he/she remains abreast of the newest medical developments. In addition, many osteopathic state societies and specialty organizations have similar continuing medical education requirements.

Licensure

The receipt of a Doctor of Osteopathy (D.O.) degree does not automatically entitle the recipient to practice as a physician and surgeon. A license is required in all states, the District of Columbia, and U.S. territories to practice as a physician and surgeon. Basically, there are three mechanisms to gain licensure: 1) the National Board of Examiners in Osteopathic Medicine and Surgery gives national boards, uniquely osteopathic, in three parts. Parts I and II are taken in school; Part III is offered graduates holding the Doctor of Osteopathy degree; 2) FLEX (the Federation Licensing Examination) is offered to both Doctors of Medicine and Doctors of Osteopathy and is administered twice annually over a three day session; and 3) individual state examinations are given by state licensing boards at various times during the year.

In regard to state licensing examinations, state requirements vary. The constituency of licensing boards thereby also varies from state to state. In some states the boards are comprised of Doctors of Osteopathy and Doctors of Medicine, and both types of physicians must take the same examination to be licensed. In other states, licensing boards are made up entirely of Doctors of Medicine while still in other jurisdictions, Doctors of Osteopathy are examined by a board solely composed of osteopathic physicians. In all states, licensure allows osteopathic physicians to provide the same range of professional services as do Doctors of Medicine. In addition, other than by further examinations, osteopathic physicians can receive a license to practice by virtue of reciprocity agreements among the states, meaning that if a physician can earn a license in a given state, he or she can set up a practice in another state without further examination if the two states have reciprocal agreements (such agreements allow physicians to relocate their practices). Physicians interested in practicing in certain states should find out whether they maintain such reciprocity agreements. In this fashion, the physician has increased opportunities to practice in whatever part of the country he or she wishes.

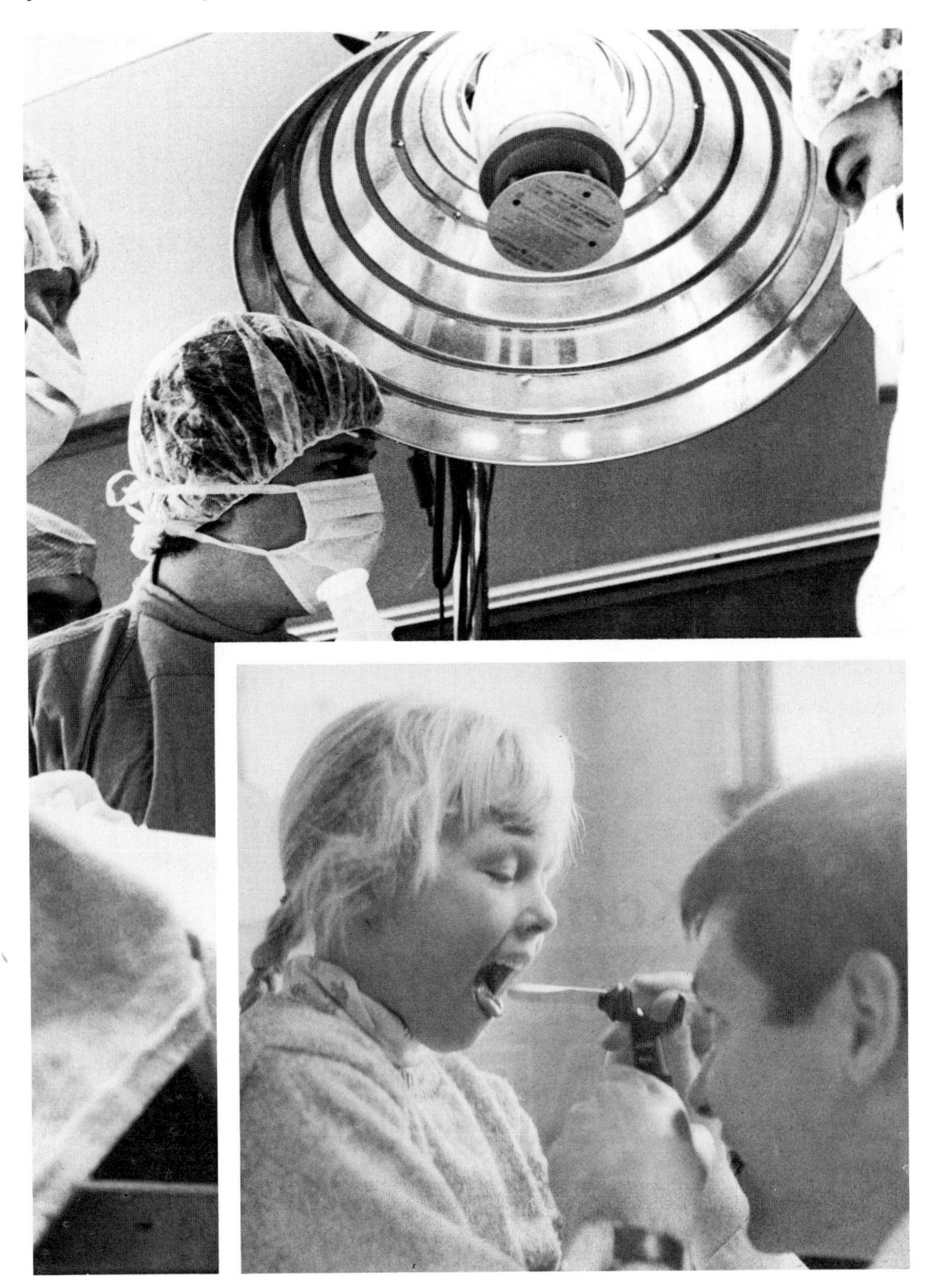

Osteopathic Practice Options

Traditionally osteopathic physicians have been viewed as family doctors. They continue to carry on that tradition as they practice primary care — delivering babies, treating the flu, and removing appendixes. Still a leading work style among D.O.s is the individual practitioner, who establishes a private office or clinic and practices either solo or in partnership with one or two other physicians. The majority of these osteopathic physicians concentrate on a primary care practice. As a primary care practitioner, the D.O.:

1. Makes first contact with the patient;
2. Makes the initial assessment/diagnosis and attempts to resolve as many of the patient's problems as possible;
3. Coordinates the activities of the various members of the total health care team including specialists, consultants, and all other ancillary health care personnel;
4. Provides continuous and consistent contact with the patient and the family;
5. Acts as the patient's advisor and confidante; and
6. Assumes continued responsibility for patient care;

Approximately 86% of osteopathic physicians specialize in the combined areas of family practice, pediatrics, obstetrics/gynecology, and general internal medicine — the traditional primary care fields.

But today as our health care system continues to evolve with new forms of health delivery mechanisms, the opportunities available to osteopathic physicians, in addition to the duties they have always performed, are many and varied. The ensuing discussion will note these various public and private options.

Today federal and state governments as well as private and public health groups recognize osteopathic medicine as a separate but equal branch of American health care. On the state and local governmental level — in towns, cities, and counties — they serve as public health officers, coroners, insurance examiners, and school team physicians. On the federal government level, many opportunities also exist for osteopathic physicians to practice medicine. Graduates of colleges of osteopathic medicine who are eligible to receive state licensure to practice medicine or osteopathy or who are approved by a body or bodies acceptable to the U.S. Secretary of Health and Human Services are eligible for appointment as commissioned medical officers in the U.S. Public Health Service. Similarly, osteopathic physicians can also receive appointments as commissioned medical officers in all the branches of the armed forces. In a related area, osteopathic physicians are also eligible for staff positions in the Department of Medicine and Surgery of the Veterans Administration if they hold the Doctor of Osteopathy degree from an accredited college of osteopathic medicine, have completed an internship, and are licensed by a state to practice medicine. For doctors who are interested in conducting medical research, osteopathic physicians are eligible for and receive grants-in-aid from the National Institutes of Health for the purpose of carrying out research projects related to cancer, heart disease, stroke, and other national health problems which come within the purview of the National Institutes.

Aside from commissioned officer positions in the U.S. Public Health Service and the armed forces, there are a number of federal agencies, in addition to that of the Veterans Administration, which use the services of osteopathic physicians. For example, osteopathic physicians can serve as aviation medical examiners for the Federal Aviation Administration. But even more importantly, the head of each government agency is authorized to establish a health service program to promote and maintain the physical and mental fitness of employees under his jurisdiction. Such health service programs may include treatment of on-the-job illness requiring emergency attention; pre-employment and other examinations; referral of employees to private medical practitioners; and preventive programs related to health. All these various services can be provided by osteopathic physicians.

As far as reimbursement is concerned, various public programs pay osteopathic physicians for their services. One such program is Medicare, the national health insurance program for the aged. Medicare provides basic protection against the cost of hospital and related post-hospital services for individuals who are 65 years or older and who are entitled to benefits under Social Security or the Railroad Retirement system. Another source of payment to osteopathic physicians derives from the activities of the Interstate Commerce Commission which requires that every interstate driver be physically examined. In addition, federal employees who are injured while in the performance of their duties are authorized to receive the services, appliances, and supplies prescribed or recommended by a qualified physician, including hospitalization.

As in the public sector, there are also many opportunities available for osteopathic physicians as our health care system continues to grow and diversify to meet the many challenges which an increasing but aging population presents. Traditional employers who hire physicians include pharmaceutical companies and insurance firms. Many private corporations also hire medical directors to oversee the medical welfare of their employees. But increasingly today, American medicine is being provided by corporations especially established for this purpose. Some of these companies own and operate their own hospitals, nursing homes, and other health facilities, while still others are solely nursing home or home health care businesses. Opportunities for physicians to work within such corporate environments are expanding. In addition, new health delivery systems called Health Maintenance Organizations (HMOs) are being established in increasing numbers. HMOs are organizations to which patients pay a monthly fee, thus entitling patients to receive a specific set of services for which additional payments are not generally required. Another growing source of medical employment for physicians are emergicenters which are established in areas of high population traffic volume like shopping centers. Providing primary care services such as physical examinations or suturing minor wounds, these centers are open almost, if not, 24 hours a day and require no appointment for treatment. Another source of medical employment are the growing number of ambulatory surgical centers. Finally, as a last example, hospice care which provides medical care, emotional support, and spiritual comfort to terminally ill patients is an additional avenue open to osteopathic physicians in which to practice their medical skills.

As can be noted, the opportunities available to osteopathic physicians to practice medicine are as diverse as they are numerous. These opportunities are likely to grow in the years ahead as the demand for medical care increases and as our population lives longer and continues to expand.

Geographically, osteopathic physicians have tended to locate mainly in Michigan, Pennsylvania, Ohio, New Jersey, Florida, Texas, and Missouri. This is due in large part to the location of the osteopathic medical colleges. There is a need for osteopathic physicians in all parts of the United States. Recently, there has been much discussion of a surplus of physicians in this country. However, this is not totally accurate as we still see a maldistribution of physicians in this country. It is just in those areas of greatest need that D.O.s tend to locate. Fifty-four percent of osteopathic physicians practice in smaller towns and rural areas.

Osteopathic Organizations

Professional organizations exist which assist members of the osteopathic medical profession in the pursuit and practice of their medical careers. These organizations address various facets of the osteopathic community: the practicing physician; the educational process; and the hospital environment.

Osteopathic Medical Practice Organizations

The largest of the organizations concerned with the practicing physician is the American Osteopathic Association (AOA), located in Chicago, Illinois. It was established in 1897 and has been in the forefront of the profession's continuing progress. The objectives of the American Osteopathic Association are to promote the public health, to encourage scientific research, and to maintain and improve standards of medical education in osteopathic colleges. The American Osteopathic Association is governed by its members, osteopathic physicians, who join local and divisional (state) societies and elect representatives to its House of Delegates. The House of Delegates, which meets annually and in which students have representation, elects the organization's officers and Board of Trustees. The organization's president, with the approval of the trustees, appoints members to serve on a long list of committees, bureaus, councils and task forces to deal with specialized functions of education, licensure, research, professional organization, accreditation, certification, publications, government liaison, and self-regulation.

The American Osteopathic Association performs a variety of functions on behalf of osteopathic physicians. It establishes policy for the profession through its House of Delegates. Its Bureau of Professional Education, which is charged with the responsibility for educational policy and accreditation, is the official accrediting body for osteopathic colleges, osteopathic hospitals, and all postdoctoral training programs. Through a number of individual specialty boards and its own Advisory Board for Osteopathic Specialists, the AOA certifies osteopathic physicians in practice areas for which they are qualified. It publishes a number of journals, magazines, and directories, and maintains membership files on all osteopathic physicians including education, formal postdoctoral programs, records for continuing education, practice patterns, and mailing addresses. The Association also conducts public relations for the profession and provides services of various sorts to its membership. A physician placement program, which matches osteopathic physicians with communities which need them, is operated by the Association.

Divisional societies of the American Osteopathic Association have been organized in every state, except Alaska. In addition, there is a divisional society for military physicians. The services of these societies vary greatly according to the osteopathic physician population in a given state. They add to the contribution of the American Osteopathic Association through programs which reflect the particular needs of their region. These voluntary associations provide necessary and often essential services to their members which include the following areas: educational, legal, organizational, administrative, public relations, legislative, membership, benefits, and professional.

In addition, there are affiliated societies of the American Osteopathic Association. One such group is the practice affiliates, most of whom are specialty colleges. The practice affiliates are all devoted to education, not just for certified specialists or residents-in-training, but for any Doctor of Osteopathy with a serious interest in the field of practice. One organization, for example, the American Academy of Osteopathy devotes its attention to the interpretation of the osteopathic perspective and the role of structural diagnosis and manipulative treatment in all branches of osteopathic medical practice. The following is a list of practice affiliates:

- American Academy of Osteopathy
- American Osteopathic College of Allergy and Immunology
- American Osteopathic College of Anesthesiologists
- American Osteopathic College of Dermatology
- American College of Osteopathic Emergency Physicians
- American College of General Practitioners in Osteopathic Medicine and Surgery
- American College of Osteopathic Internists
- American College of Neuropsychiatrists
- American Osteopathic College of Nuclear Medicine
- American College of Osteopathic Obstetricians and Gynecologists
- Osteopathic College of Ophthalmology and Otorhinolaryngology
- American Osteopathic Academy of Orthopedics
- American Osteopathic College of Pathologists
- American College of Osteopathic Pediatricians
- American Osteopathic College of Proctology, Inc.
- American Osteopathic College of Preventive Medicine
- American Osteopathic College of Radiology
- American Osteopathic College of Rehabilitation Medicine
- American Osteopathic College of Rheumatology, Inc.
- American Osteopathic College of Sclerotherapy, Inc.
- American Osteopathic Academy of Sports Medicine
- American College of Osteopathic Surgeons

These specialty colleges all provide education and information which is also important to Doctors of Osteopathy in other areas of practice.

Nonpractice Osteopathic Organizations

In addition to the previously listed organizations there are several nonpractice groups which are dedicated to the support and advancement of better public health through service to the osteopathic medical profession. Each group devotes special attention to a particular field such as colleges or hospitals, thereby providing services to the entire osteopathic medical profession and the public it serves. The principal concern of the nonpractice affiliates is education. Among their numerous programs are those directed toward meeting predoctoral and postdoctoral training needs at all levels and in a wide variety of settings. Other programs are designed to distribute information about state and federal health care programs and legislation as they affect students, hospital personnel, and practicing physicians. Still other programs aim at providing funds for osteopathic medical education or providing information about public health programs. The following is a list of nonpractice affiliates:

- Auxiliary to the American Osteopathic Association
- American Association of Colleges of Osteopathic Medicine
- Academy of Osteopathic Directors of Medical Education
- American Association of Osteopathic Examiners
- American Osteopathic Hospital Association
- National Board of Examiners for Osteopathic Physicians and Surgeons, Inc.
- Association of Osteopathic State Executive Directors

The American Association of Colleges of Osteopathic Medicine (AACOM) is the primary organization concerned with undergraduate osteopathic medical education, and is dedicated to its advancement and enrichment. The Association serves osteopathic medical colleges and their students in a concerted effort to fulfill common objectives. When initially founded in 1897, the American Association of Colleges of Osteopathic Medicine consisted of college administrators meeting to discuss common problems and issues. Today the Association, an institutional membership comprised of the fifteen osteopathic medical colleges in the United States, is involved in numerous diverse activities and is an integral part of a dynamic and growing profession.

As the number of osteopathic medical colleges has grown, so too has AACOM. Today the Association, guided by its Board of Governors, Council of Deans and various other councils and committees, is actively involved in all issues of osteopathic medical education. The services that the Association provides to its members and the public are as follows:

- Aspects of osteopathic medical education are frequently studied and the information is made available through the Association. Often the Association joins other health professions in forming a collective voice to express the position of the institutions which are training health professionals to meet the nation's future health needs. This has included studies on subjects such as geriatric programs at the osteopathic medical colleges, student indebtedness, clinical competency objectives for osteopathic medical students, financial aid, and statistical data on the colleges.

- The Association carefully monitors the activities of the U.S. Congress and the federal agencies in order to assist in the planning and development of the nation's resources.

- Individuals seeking admission to colleges of osteopathic medicine can file one application with the Association's centralized application service (AACOMAS). Currently, thirteen colleges of osteopathic medicine participate in this service which verifies and distributes information to the colleges designated by the applicant.

- Programs and activities to improve the opportunities for minority and disadvantaged groups are a vital segment of the Association's activities.

The American Osteopathic Hospital Association is the primary association concerned with the hospitals' role in the osteopathic and general community. Its purpose is to promote public health and welfare through effective hospital leadership. It provides a collective voice in areas of common interest for member hospitals. Management services and programs are provided to members which assist them in improving their ability to deliver quality osteopathic medical care. The association also collects and analyzes data relevant to its mission, and publishes a directory of hospitals providing postdoctoral training (internships and residencies).

A final group of nonpractice affiliates to the American Osteopathic Association are the philanthropic affiliates. These include:

- The American Osteopathic Foundation
- The Osteopathic Trust
- The National Osteopathic Foundation

The most active of the American Osteopathic Association's philanthropic affiliates is the National Osteopathic Foundation. Its programs include the Osteopathic Seals Program, proceeds of which are divided between research and student loans, and the Education Grants Program, with funds for postdoctoral education provided through the pharmaceutical industry. Also included is the Osteopathic Progress Fund, a unique program started by the osteopathic profession in 1942 to raise funds from the members of the profession for the support of its colleges.

All the previous groups constitute a vast array of support for the osteopathic physician. Without exception, their intent is to provide quality resources for the expansion and effectiveness of osteopathic medicine. This, in turn, improves the quality of medical care that patients receive and the quality of their lives. The existence of these many support groups for the osteopathic physician only enriches the quality of medical care that is delivered in the United States.

162

Admission Requirements

Osteopathic medical education is not something different — it is something extra. The osteopathic medical curriculum covers virtually the same areas of study as other medical education. But unlike the allopathic medical student, the osteopathic medical student spends an additional 300-500 hours of training in manipulative treatment. However, before the prospective doctor can practice his/her medical art, he or she must first be admitted to an osteopathic medical college to learn it. The ensuing discussion tells how.

Admission to a college of osteopathic medicine requires a minimum of three years of preprofessional education in a college or university which is accredited by a regional educational association. In 1984, on the average, 99% of the students enrolled in osteopathic medical colleges held a bachelor's degree. The most popular undergraduate major of those applying to the osteopathic medical colleges was biology at 39%; followed by chemistry at 8.5% and psychology at 6.8%. Many other majors were represented: sciences, nursing, mathematics, humanities, social sciences, theatre, business, and religion. Other applicants have graduate degrees in one of the biological sciences at approximately 42%, psychology at 5.9%, and others are in public health, science, or other health professions. In this regard, during the 1984-85 academic year 12% of the freshmen had already earned graduate degrees prior to their admission to colleges of osteopathic medicine.

In general, an entering student must have a minimum credit of 6 semester hours in English, with 12 recommended; a full year's work in physics, biology, inorganic and organic chemistry (one year each); and elective courses reflecting a broad liberal arts background. All prospective students should take the Medical College Admission Test (MCAT), offered twice each year in the fall and spring. (It is important to check each school's requirement as to the date that the MCAT should be taken.) The MCAT evaluates a student's potential for success in osteopathic or allopathic medical school and is an important consideration for acceptance. For the osteopathic medical colleges, the minimum competitive standards are a "B" average for undergraduate work and MCAT scores above 7 (out of a possible 15). In the 1984-1985 academic year, the mean grade point average of first year students was 3.25; for the prior year it had been 3.23. MCAT scores remained fairly stable from 1979 to 1984. For the 1984 entering class, they were 8.3 for biology, 7.6 for chemistry, 7.7 for physics, 7.6 for science problems, 7.8 for reading, and 7.3 for quantitative examinations. In 1983, there were about three applicants for each available space in osteopathic colleges.

In addition to taking the Medical College Admission Test, students are required to submit to colleges of osteopathic medicine letters of recommendation from their undergraduate colleges. Admission committees are interested in evidence of leadership and the student's ability to get along with people, both peers and instructors. They also look for examples of dependability, maturity, and integrity in both academic and extracurricular areas of the student's life. The jobs students hold in undergraduate schools are considered in the same light as extracurricular activities. Although relevant work or volunteer experience is an advantage, it is not a requirement. A personal interview is mandatory and an important part of the admission decision. And again, colleges of osteopathic medicine are interested in the applicant's motivation. During the past several years, students have considered the following two factors as being important in choosing a career in osteopathic medicine: an inherent desire to be of help to people, and interests and attitudes which make it natural to pursue this field in preference to others. In addition, an interview and/or a recommendation by an osteopathic physician may be required as part of the admission procedure. If the latter is an admission requirement, the prospective student should check with the osteopathic college, the American Association of Colleges of Osteopathic Medicine, or the state osteopathic association if he/she does not know an osteopathic physician who can provide such a recommendation.

Osteopathic medical colleges have an interest in selecting students who are informed about osteopathic medicine and are truly motivated toward a medical career, particularly a career in osteopathic medicine. In deciding whether to apply to colleges of osteopathic medicine, it is absolutely essential that the applicant be familiarized with the background, methods, and other characteristics of the profession. The applicant must also be aware of the characteristics and philosophy unique to the particular school to which he/she is applying. Remember, the osteopathic medical profession has an outspoken commitment to family, community, and preventive medicine. If a student approaches osteopathic medicine at all, it should be with this kind of interest in mind.

Another relevant factor in applying to osteopathic medical colleges is state residence. Although historically colleges of osteopathic medicine were independently supported, in recent years they have drawn increasingly upon financial support from state government. As with allopathic medical, dental, and veterinary schools, state supported or state assisted osteopathic medical colleges have given admission preference to state residents. Given financial pressures upon medical education of all kinds, the trend appears to be toward more such state restrictions. During the 1982-83 academic year, 55% of the students attended osteopathic medical colleges in the state of their home residence. Some colleges of osteopathic medicine are also regional centers of osteopathic medical education.

Total enrollment in osteopathic medical colleges continues to rise. During the 1982-1983 academic year, there were 5,822 students enrolled, 10% more than the previous year. The number of women attending osteopathic medical schools also continues to rise. Now 25% of first year enrollees are women, compared to 3% in 1970. About one of every five graduating osteopathic physicians is a woman. Likewise, members of the ethnic minority groups are gradually entering the osteopathic medical profession. From 1976 to 1983, the actual number of minority students had more than doubled from 155 to 355. Included in this group are Black Americans, American Indian/American Native, Hispanics, and Asian Americans/Pacific Islanders. Osteopathic colleges tend to be more liberal than allopathic medical schools in accepting applicants who are not matriculating right out of undergraduate college. The average age of first-year osteopathic students is 25 years old. These students are perceived as excellent candidates for osteopathic medical colleges as their varied perspectives, backgrounds, and knowledge enrich and expand the total class experience.

To find out more about taking the Medical College Admission Test which is required for applying to a college of osteopathic medicine, students can contact their college or university testing offices or write directly to the Medical College Admission Test (MCAT) Registration, The American College Testing Program, P.O. Box 414, Iowa City, Iowa 52240.

After the MCAT is taken, the student can begin the process of applying to a college of osteopathic medicine. The American Association of Colleges of Osteopathic Medicine provides a centralized application service called AACOMAS, in which applications are processed for 13 of the 15 osteopathic medical colleges in the country. The student only has to fill out one application and submit one set of transcripts to apply to one or thirteen colleges. Information on applying to the osteopathic medical colleges and an application form may be obtained by writing to: AACOMAS, 6110 Executive Boulevard, Suite 405, Rockville, Maryland 20852. After applicants are screened from their AACOMAS application, MCAT scores, and educational achievements, they are considered for campus interviews and admittance to a college of osteopathic medicine. Applicants to the two schools not included in AACOMAS should submit applications directly to these two schools.

Chicago College of Osteopathic Medicine

5200 South Ellis Avenue
Chicago, Illinois 60615
Telephone: (312) 947-4725

Year Founded: 1900

Status: Private, with some state support

Background: The Chicago College of Osteopathic Medicine (CCOM) is situated in Hyde Park a residential district, located in one of the major educational and cultural sections of the city of Chicago. Hyde Park is a complete community, having churches of all faiths, numerous banking facilities, clubs, theatres, beaches, golf courses, and athletic parks. The college is located immediately north of the University of Chicago campus and is approximately seven miles from the downtown central business district of Chicago.

While the basic curriculum of the College conforms to accepted medical standards as to length and content, the standard medical curriculum is oriented in this college toward a more thorough appreciation and understanding of structural relationships, the integrating functions of the nervous systems, and the influence of physical forces and injuries in predisposing to disease. Characteristic techniques and skills in dealing with the neuro-musculo-skeletal components of disease are also a distinctive part of the course of training.

The college primarily uses three Chicago Osteopathic Medical Centers in the training of its students. The major educational training center is located in Hyde Park and consists of a basic science building, a 297-bed hospital and an outpatient clinic which offers excellent medical care to 200,000 outpatients a year. Another educational medical center is located in Olympia Fields and is a new ultra-modern 201 bed complex. A third teaching hospital, Louise Burg with 120 beds, is located in the center city district. In addition to its three medical centers, the Chicago College of Osteopathic Medicine operates eleven outreach clinics in both rural and inner city areas.

The college faculty consists of 245 physicians and research scientists. The osteopathic medical education is rich in clinical experiences; 105 weeks in rotation at its various teaching centers comprise the junior and senior years. Opportunities for professional growth are extended to postdoctoral students. Emphasis is placed on the important practice of family medicine reflecting the profession's holistic approach to education and medical practice.

Student Applicants: The Chicago College of Osteopathic Medicine receives an average of 2,000 applications annually for 100 seats. Approximately one-half of each entering class consists of Illinois residents. The Admissions Committee seeks students with proven academic ability which would insure success in pursuing a strong medical curriculum. Also evaluated is the applicant's osteopathic interest and understanding as well as his/her extra academic achievements which must indicate an ability to relate to people and serve them. The Chicago College of Osteopathic Medicine is committed to affirmative action.

Entrance Requirements:

- Achievement in required courses must be at least 2.0 on a 4.0 scale. No student will be considered with less than a 2.5 cumulative average on a 4.0 scale. However, to be competitive, an applicant should demonstrate academic ability well beyond the above listed requirements.
- A minimum of 90 semester hours of undergraduate credit in a regionally accredited college or university is required for consideration as an applicant. B.S. or B.A. degrees are recommended.
- The New Medical College Admission Test is required.
- Students accepted for admission must have completed the following prerequisites prior to matriculation: one academic year or its equivalent in English, physics, biology, general chemistry, and organic chemistry.
- It is desirable that the elective courses afford a broad educational/cultural background. Courses in the humanities and social sciences are recommended, in addition to courses in the biological sciences such as zoology, anatomy, embryology, histology, biochemistry, microbiology and general physiology.

Admissions Process: The Chicago College of Osteopathic Medicine uses a rolling admissions policy. Admissions to a class are determined from interviews held between October and mid-March. As candidates are interviewed, seats are filled and candidates are notified. The process proceeds progressively until the class is filled.

Application Deadline: The annual application deadline is December 1. Applications are filed through AACOMAS.

Tuition 1984-1985: In-state residents, $9,600; Out-of-state residents, $12,775. (All fees are included, but tuition is subject to change anytime. Tuition charges include laboratory, student activities, comprehensive examination, and graduation fees.)

Total Enrollment 1984-1985: 396

Minority Applicant/Admissions Statistics: Unavailable

Principal Contacts:

Thaddeus P. Kawalek, Ph.D., President
Thomas W. Allen, D.O., Dean and Vice President for Academic Affairs
Harold L. Hakes, Ph.D., J.D., Dean of Students and Director of Admissions

College of Osteopathic Medicine of the Pacific

College Plaza
Pomona, California 91766-1889
Telephone: (714) 623-6116

Year Founded: 1977

Status: Private

Background: The College of Osteopathic Medicine of the Pacific (COMP) is an independent, freestanding, non-profit institution of higher education located in Pomona, about 35 miles east of Los Angeles, near the foothills of the San Gabriel Mountains. It is an area which has a high concentration of private and state colleges and universities. Mountain resorts are nearby and Pacific Ocean beaches, the desert, Hollywood, Pasadena, Los Angeles, arboretums, theme parks, museums, art galleries, theatres and concert halls are all within an hour's drive.

The mission of the College is to educate primary care physicians in the osteopathic tradition, and it is dedicated to the health care and medical education needs of the West. The College conducts a four-year curriculum organized in semesters, and stresses the interdependence of the biological, clinical, behavioral, and social sciences. The hallmark of the program is the integration of the social and biological sciences so that the human and clinical skills of the osteopathic medical students can be enhanced. The first two years of the curriculum are taught in the Academic Center and South Campus building in Pomona with clinical instruction and field experience on campus and in the surrounding area. The last two years are utilized for the clerkship program in osteopathic and mixed staff hospitals and other clinical facilities in California and Western states. The College of Osteopathic Medicine of the Pacific through its formalized Clinical Network called COMPNET currently operates five medical centers, two in Pomona (within one mile of the College) and three in the San Diego area. All COMPNET medical facilities are operated as family practice outpatient medical centers, which serve the needs of the community, provide clinical training for COMP students, and future practice opportunities for COMP graduates. Current plans call for the addition of at least one medical center per year to the College's clinical networks.

Student Applicants: The College will accept applications for admission from all qualified candidates, with preference given to residents of the western United States: Alaska, Arizona, California, Colorado, Hawaii, Idaho, Montana, Nevada, New Mexico, North Dakota, Oregon, South Dakota, Utah, Washington, and Wyoming. The College receives applications from more qualified students than can be admitted, and non-academic criteria are important in making the selection. The size of the 1984 entering class was 100 students. While grades and test scores are important in the process of selecting candidates for admission and may suggest future academic success, the Admissions Committee of the College recognizes that these statistics, by themselves, do not guarantee later success as a physician. The College seeks a diverse yet balanced student population and considers such factors as unusual background, work experiences, letters of recommendation, interest in osteopathic medicine, and professional promise. To ascertain these factors, a personal interview with the Admissions Committee is required before acceptance is given. The College may exercise its discretion to rely upon additional considerations. The College selects its students and administers all of its programs without discrimination as to race, creed, sex, national origin or non-qualifying handicap.

Entrance Requirements

- A minimum grade point average of 2.5 on a 4.0 scale, overall as well as in the sciences, must be attained. Applicants should be aware that the average GPA for the entering classes at COMP has been above 3.20 in the sciences and overall.

- A minimum of 90 semester hours, or three-fourths of the credits required for a baccalaureate degree, from an accredited college or university. The majority of candidates accepted for admission will have completed four or more years of preprofessional study prior to matriculation.

- Scores from the New Medical College Admission Test (MCAT) must be submitted.
- All applicants must complete a full academic year or its equivalent in inorganic chemistry, organic chemistry, biology, physics, English, and behavioral sciences.

Admissions Process: Upon receipt of all supplementary materials, including a minimum of three letters of recommendation, the Admission Committee grants interviews to the best candidates. Interviews are granted from September through April and acceptances are offered starting in October. Interview day activities last the entire day. Candidates can maximize their chances of being competitive by submitting all the required application materials early in the admissions process.

Application Deadline: The annual application deadline is December 1. Applications are filed through AACOMAS.

Tuition: $12,500

Total Enrollment 1984-1985: 360

Minority Applicant/Admissions Statistics:

	1983-1984			
	Black Americans	American Indians/ American Natives	Hispanics	Asian Americans/ Pacific Islanders
First Year Enrolled	3	1	7	4
Total Enrolled	7	4	11	19

Principal Contact:

Philip Pumerantz, Ph.D., President
O. J. Bailes, D.O., Dean of Academic Affairs
Curt Clauss, Director of Admissions

Kirksville College of Osteopathic Medicine

800 West Jefferson Street
Kirksville, Missouri 63501
Telephone: (816) 626-2121

Year Founded: 1892

Status: Private

Background: The Kirksville College of Osteopathic Medicine (KCOM) is located in the city of 20,000 population in Northeastern Missouri, approximately 70 miles west of the Mississippi River and 30 miles south of the Iowa state line. The school was established as the first college of osteopathic medicine under its original name, the American School of Osteopathy, and has trained a substantial number of practicing osteopathic physicians.

Main college buildings include ten structures used for instructional, clinical, administrative, and research purposes. Additional buildings include those for student housing, a student campus center, a day-care center, heating, maintenance and housekeeping, and three of historical interest — the cabin birthplace of its founder, Andrew Taylor Still, M.D., the first classroom, and the Still National Osteopathic Museum. Seven extension clinics are maintained in nearby rural communities. College-owned facilities are supplemented by the Twin Pines Adult Care Center which is a geriatric unit, and ten affiliated hospitals in Arizona, Indiana, Michigan, Missouri, Ohio, and Oklahoma.

The curricular plan of the college consists of four years of study leading to the Doctor of Osteopathy degree (D.O.). It is designed to produce osteopathic physicians who will be well prepared for the problems of general family practice. Each of the first two years is of nine months duration and is divided into three quarters devoted primarily to the basic medical sciences with clinical exposure beginning in the second year in a local nursing home. The third year of study is six months of clinically oriented courses with concurrent nursing home experience. The fourth year consists of fifteen months and begins immediately following the third year. It includes four months of study in the college's outpatient and rural extension clinics, four months of clinical training in general hospitals, and five months of electives.

Student Applicants: As a private institution, the Kirksville College of Osteopathic Medicine is seeking students from all parts of the United States who are interested in a

career in osteopathic medicine. A Minority Recruitment Program was established in 1974. The college is actively seeking to graduate capable physicians from minority groups that are inadequately represented in today's current physician manpower pool.

Applicants are screened initially for intellectual qualifications in an attempt to select those individuals capable of meeting the college's academic standards. A further selection is made on the basis of character, personality, and interest in the distinctive aspects of osteopathic medicine. Applicants who reach the final phase of the selection process may be invited to visit the school for an interview with the Admissions Committee. All applicants selected for admission are interviewed before acceptance.

Entrance Requirements:

- Applicants must have achieved a minimum of 2.5 out of a possible 4.0 pre-professional grade point average overall, as well as in the sciences. Applicants should be aware that the grade point average for the 1985 entering class was above 3.25.

- A minimum of 90 semester hours or three-fourths of the credit required for a degree at a college or university granting baccalaureate degrees and accredited by a regional educational association. Most of those accepted for admission will have completed the baccalaureate degree.

- The New Medical College Admission Test is required.

- Applicants must have completed one full academic year or the equivalent in each of the following: English; biology, must include laboratory and a basic course in general biology or general zoology; physics, must include laboratory and cover the study of mechanics, sound, heat, magnetism, electricity and light; inorganic chemistry, must include laboratory; organic chemistry, must include laboratory and cover the study of aliphatic and benzene compounds. Elective subjects should afford a broad educational and cultural background as recommended by the applicant's pre-professional advisor. Courses in biochemistry and comparative or human anatomy are recommended.

Admissions Process: To receive full consideration a candidate should apply early and see that all required materials are submitted as early as possible in the admissions cycle. As candidates are interviewed, seats are filled and candidates notified. The process continues until the class is filled. The size of the 1985 entering class was 132 students.

Application Deadline: The annual application deadline is December 1. Applications are filed through AACOMAS.

Tuition: $14,000 (Tuition is subject to change. Tuition charges include health insurance and fees).

Total Enrollment 1984-1985: 533

Minority Applicant/Admissions Statistics:

	1984-1985			
	Black Americans	American Indians/ American Natives	Hispanics	Asian Americans/ Pacific Islanders
First Year Enrolled	1	0	2	1
Total Enrolled	6	2	7	11

Principal Contacts:

Fred C. Tinning, Ph.D., President
James R. Stookey, D.O., Dean and Vice President for Academic Affairs
Francis M. Walter, M.Ed., Dean of Students

Michigan State University College of Osteopathic Medicine

East Fee Hall
East Lansing, Michigan 48824
Telephone: (517) 355-9611

Year Founded: 1969

Status: Public, State Supported

Background: The College of Osteopathic Medicine opened in 1969 as a private college in Pontiac, Michigan, under the sponsorship of the Michigan Association of Osteopathic Physicians and Surgeons. Also in 1969, the Michigan legislature authorized the first state-supported college of osteopathic medicine in the United States. After legislative action, the College of Osteopathic Medicine in 1971 became a unit of Michigan State University thereby becoming the first state-supported and university-based school of its kind.

Michigan State University College of Osteopathic Medicine's curriculum presents material in a coordinated manner so that students can better understand the basic processes of the human body, integrate a concept of the functions of bodily systems and see their clinical applications. Clinical training is included at every level, progressing in difficulty as the student moves up the curriculum spiral, adding topical information and reinforcing concepts at every level. The curriculum includes eight quarters of an integrated basic science and clinical program and a study of individual body systems, and five quarters of clinical clerkships, including ambulatory and inpatient care, in community hospitals and health-care agencies. Michigan State University's Clinical Center provides an opportunity for both allopathic and osteopathic medical students to pursue ambulatory and research interests. The theories and applications of manipulative techniques are included at all levels of the curriculum, increasing in complexity as the student progresses through the program.

In addition to the Doctor of Osteopathy degree (D.O.), the college also offers a combined D.O./Ph.D. study. This program is designed to prepare academicians and researchers for osteopathic medical education. This Medical Scientist Training Program is aimed for a small number of highly qualified trainees who may obtain both degrees either simultaneously or sequentially. Applicants must have demonstrated research productivity, academic excellence, motivation to pursue graduate and medical study over an extended period of years, and acceptance into both the medical and science programs. Opportunity is also available for interested but less experienced D.O. students to undertake research for a short term, without Ph.D. study. For both opportunities, financial stipends are awarded competitively for the support of research training and graduate study, but not the medical training or study.

Student Applicants: Legislative requirements ensure 80 percent of each entering class of 125 to be Michigan residents. Approximately 300 students are invited to interview for 125 seats. Out-of-state applicants, therefore, face very strong competition for the remaining class openings. The college seeks to increase the admissions of members of ethnic minority and other underrepresented populations in medicine.

General characteristics sought are academic excellence, a high degree of unselfishness and effectiveness with others, knowledge of and interest in osteopathic medicine, maturity, ability to communicate verbally and in writing. Specific characteristics additionally sought for those pursuing a career in academic medicine are creative thought and motivation for research and scholarship. Students who have the desire and aptitude to become osteopathic physicians but who have experienced unequal educational opportunities for social, cultural or racial reasons are especially urged to apply.

Entrance Requirements:

- A minimum science grade average of 2.5 on a 4.0 scale and an overall grade point average of 2.5. Preference is given to those candidates who have completed all requirements at the time of application.

- A minimum 2.0 grade point average at the time of application, with no grade below a 2.0, is required in each of the following disciplines: biology (8 semester hours or 12 quarter hours); English (6 semester hours or 9 quarter hours); psychological-social-behavioral science (6 semester hours or 9 quarter hours). It is expected that labs will be included in each of basic sciences.

- A minimum of 90 semester hours required for a baccalaureate degree from an accredited college or university. 96 percent of the students entering the program have baccalaureate degrees and approximately 35 percent of these have advanced degrees.

- The New Medical College Admission Test is required.

Admissions Process: Each application is evaluated on two major criteria — strength of candidate's academic preparation and a well-documented ability to successfully meet the emotional, social, and physical needs of others. Students are offered interviews after secondary applications are submitted and evaluated. In 1983, the College of Osteopathic Medicine used a weighted evaluation system in determining, first, who is to be interviewed and second, who will be admitted. The weightings for academic and non-academic performance are established each year by the Admissions Committee.

Application Deadline: The annual application deadline is November 1. Applications are filed through AACOMAS. Prospective students are urged to apply during the summer months and the early fall.

Tuition: In-state residents, $5,200; Out-of-state residents, $10,500. (Tuition is subject to change.)

Minority Applicant/Admissions Statistics:

	1982-1983			
	Black Americans	American Indians/ American Natives	Hispanics	Asian Americans/ Pacific Islanders
First Year Enrolled	9	3	3	4
Total Enrolled	30	6	9	20

Principal Contacts:

Myron S. Magen, D.O., Dean
Philip E. Greenman, D.O., Associate Dean
Elissa L. Gatlin, Ph.D., Director of Admissions

University of New England College of Osteopathic Medicine

11 Hills Beach Road
Biddeford, Maine 04005
Telephone: (207) 283-0171

Year Founded: 1978

Status: Private

Background: The University of New England College of Osteopathic Medicine (UNECOM) is a non-profit institution that has as its primary objective the training of osteopathic physicians who will practice in the underserved areas of New England. Located in Biddeford on the southern coast of Maine, the College of Osteopathic Medicine shares the campus with an undergraduate liberal arts college and the College of Health Sciences.

The school not only emphasizes the training of family practice physicians but also as a distinctive feature of medical education, focuses on preventive medicine: students are trained not only to care for the sick but also to participate with their patients to promote health.

The two-and-one-half year on-campus portion of the program is primarily didactic. The first year curriculum emphasizes instruction in the core of the basic sciences. In the second-and-one-half year, the curriculum shifts from the discipline focus to an integrated "body system" approach, wherein the impact of the various disciplines is integrated with the clinical sciences into each body system. To accomplish the school's specific purposes, the two-and-one-half year curriculum places consistent emphasis on osteopathic principles and manipulative practice, human behavior, community health and health maintenance, and the humanities. From the beginning of their first year, all students observe and later experience clinical practice through part-time clinical preceptorships. Beginning in January of their third year, students begin 16 months of full-time hospital-based clerkships and office-based preceptorships. This off-campus clinical training takes place in over 20 college affiliated community hospitals and medical centers throughout the Northeast. Consistent with the college's emphasis on health maintenance and family practice, several of the full-time clinical experiences are in ambulatory-care clinics. Students have the option for three of the 16 months to self-select hospital rotations and sites and to submit these to the college for approval.

Student Applicants: Students are considered on the basis of their demonstrated academic abilities as well as references that support a demonstrated emotional capability to function as an osteopathic family practitioner. Candidates are expected to be familiar with the philosophy and practice of osteopathic medicine. The college will accept applications for admission from all qualified candidates with preference being given to New England residents and those oriented toward practice in New England. In addition to demonstrating academic ability, the successful candidate must have personal qualities that can be developed into those skills deemed absolutely essential to the practice of osteopathic family medicine as demonstrated through background, work experiences, letters of recommendation, social and cultural involvements, and personal interviews. The school is actively seeking to graduate competent physicians from minority groups that are inadequately served by and represented in today's current physician manpower.

Entrance Requirements:

- A minimum grade point average of 2.5 on a 4.0 scale.
- Each applicant must have completed at least 75 percent credit toward a baccalaureate degree from a regionally accredited college or university.
- The New Medical College Admissions Test is required.
- One academic year of each of the following is required: English composition and literature, general chemistry, organic chemistry, physics, and biology. It is expected that labs will be included in each of the basic sciences. Applicants are encouraged to enroll in additional courses to broaden their science background and to elect non-science courses that will provide a broad-based education in the humanities and social sciences.

Admissions Process: Interviews are required prior to admission. Interviews are granted only upon invitation of the Admissions Committee. As candidates are interviewed, seats are filled and candidates notified. To receive full consideration, applicants should make certain to submit all required materials as early as possible. The interview process begins in mid-fall of the year preceding admission. In 1984 the size of the entering class was 70 students.

Application Deadline: The annual application deadline is December 1. Applications are filed through AACOMAS.

Tuition: $12,000 (Tuition is subject to change by action of the University Board).

Total Enrollment 1984-1985: 274

Minority Applicant/Admissions Statistics: Unavailable

Principal Contacts:

Charles W. Ford, Ph.D., President
Martyn E. Richardson, D.O., Dean for Academic Affairs
Lisa H. Lacroix, Director of Admissions

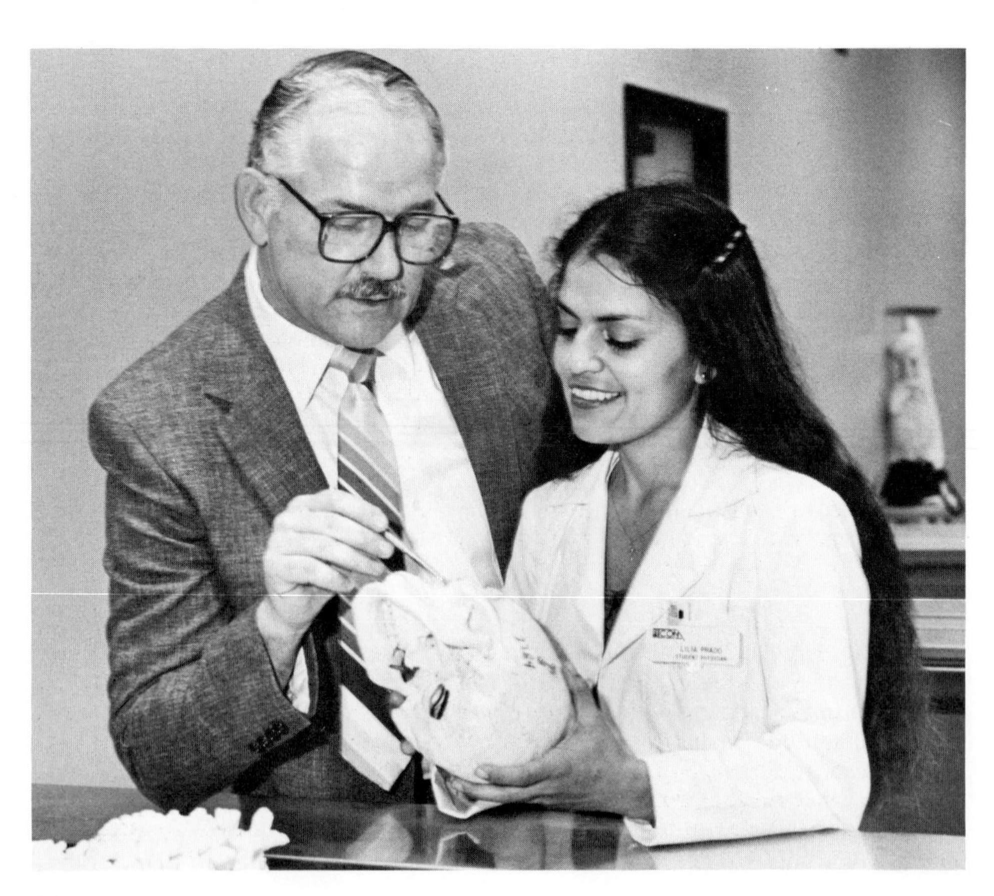

University of Medicine and Dentistry of New Jersey — School of Osteopathic Medicine

401 Haddon Avenue
Camden, New Jersey 08103
Telephone: (609) 757-7700

Year Founded: 1976

Status: Public, State Supported

Background: The School of Osteopathic Medicine, one of the Divisions of the University of Medicine and Dentistry of New Jersey (UMDNJ), was established by an Act of the Legislature of the State of New Jersey. The school's Admission Office is located in Stratford, New Jersey, and the basic science training is provided initially at the University of Medicine and Dentistry of New Jersey's Rutgers Medical School in Piscataway, New Jersey, by faculties of both the Rutgers Medical School and the School of Osteopathic Medicine. The clinical components of the curriculum are based in the three divisions of Kennedy Memorial Hospitals-University Medical Center.

Committed to a holistic approach in patient care, the school provides a medical education that fully trains students in the principles of scientific medicine, while emphasizing the inter-relation between structure and function in explaining the disease process.

Student Applicants: The Admissions Committee selects students primarily from among qualified New Jersey applicants and a small number from other states who are committed to a holistic approach to the care of patients. Emphasis is given to demonstrated scholastic aptitude, motivation, character, emotional maturity, and an ability to communicate and relate easily with others. All applicants shall be considered without prejudice in regard to race, religion, sex, or ethnic background. Applications are especially welcomed from qualified persons from minority groups currently underrepresented in the osteopathic profession.

Entrance Requirements:

- In-state residents: A minimum grade point average of 3.0 on a 4.0 scale in both science and non-science areas. Out-of-state residents are not encouraged to apply with less than a 3.4 overall grade point average.

- Accepted applicants must have completed a baccalaureate degree from an accredited college or university at time of matriculation.

- Scores from the New Medical College Admission Test (MCAT) are required and are to be taken no later than the fall of the application year.

- Required academic work will include: two years of biological laboratory courses; one year of physics; inorganic and organic chemistry, each with laboratories; one year of college level math — one semester may be satisfied with a course in computer science or statistics (calculus is highly recommended); one year of English which must include one semester of English composition (one year of English composition is strongly recommended); and one year of behavioral sciences. Additional recommended courses include: history, philosophy, religion, and the arts; knowledge of modern language is advisable; additional science courses beyond the minimum required.

Admissions Process: Selected applicants are invited for an interview beginning in October. A small number of students are selected monthly from October through March. The class is filled and an alternate list is established by April 1. The size of the 1984 entering class was 56 students.

Application Deadline: The annual application deadline is December 1. Applications are filed through AACOMAS.

Tuition: In-state residents, $7,175; Out-of-state residents, $8,965. (The amount of tuition is subject to change.)

Total Enrollment 1984-1985: 219

Minority Applicant/Admissions Statistics:

	1983-1984			
	Black Americans	American Indians/ American Natives	Hispanics	Asian Americans/ Pacific Islanders
First Year Enrolled	1	0	4	4
Total Enrolled	1	0	9	7

Principal Contacts:

Gerald Scharf, D.O., Acting Dean
Robert L. Thompson, Ed.D., Associate Dean for Student Affairs and Admissions
Malcolm J. Keiter, Admissions Officer
(Located at UMDNJ-SOM, 40 East Laurel Road, Stratford, New Jersey 08084.)

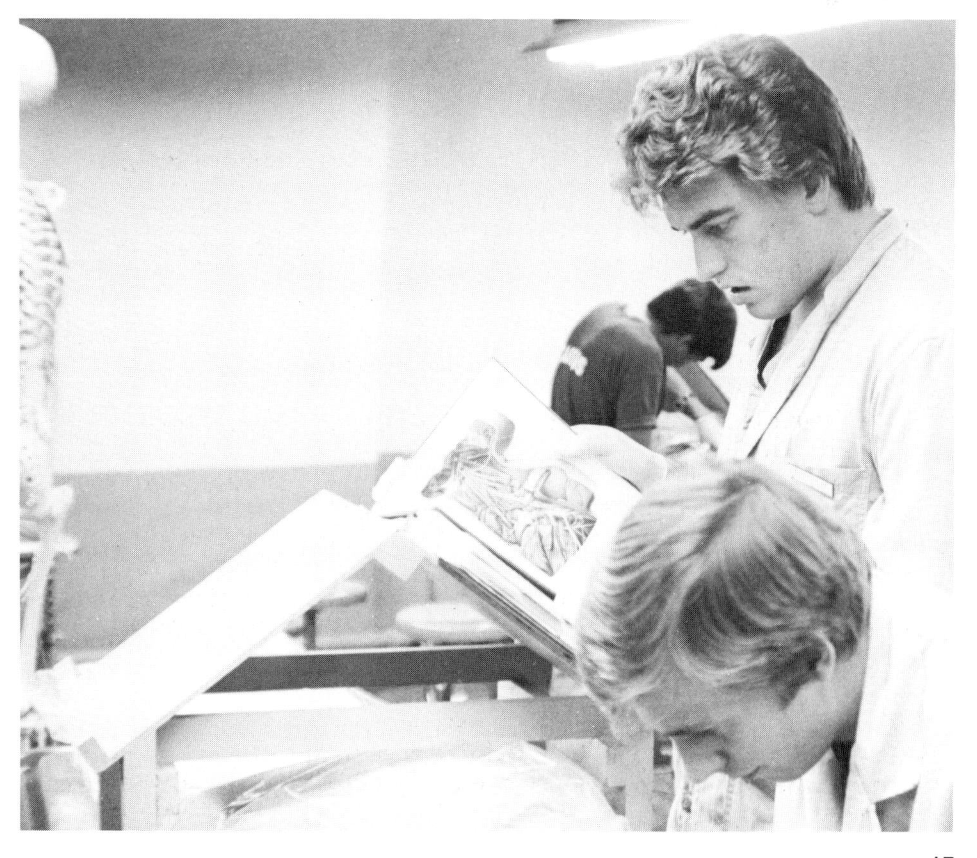

New York College of Osteopathic Medicine of New York Institute of Technology

Old Westbury, New York 11568
Telephone: (516) 626-6900

Year Founded: 1976

Status: Private

Background: The New York College of Osteopathic Medicine is located on the scenic 750-acre Westbury campus of the New York Institute of Technology in Old Westbury, a suburban community on the North Shore of Long Island, some 25 miles east of New York City. The New York metropolitan area is unparalleled in its cultural and recreational offerings. Because the area is one of the major health care centers in the United States, it constitutes an additional education resource for the College's medical program. Leading practitioners and researchers lecture at the College during the academic year.

The New York College of Osteopathic Medicine, the first school of osteopathic medicine in New York State, is dedicated to predoctoral and postdoctoral education of osteopathic physicians, the fostering of careers in family medicine, and research on human health and disease, with a focus on the roles of the neuromuscular and musculoskeletal systems. The curriculum emphasizes needs and opportunities in primary health care and community health services, particularly health care problems of the inner city and smaller communities, and encompasses two years of pre-clinical and didactic clinical course work, followed by two years devoted to clinical clerkships.

NYCOM's curriculum is geared not only to osteopathic primary care, but other areas of interest to family practitioners as well, including specialties such as internal medicine, pediatrics, obstetrics, family practice, and psychiatry.

Intensive coursework in osteopathic principles and practice, forming a foundation for the entire curriculum of NYCOM, is given during the first two years of the program. The student-physician gradually develops an ability to perform satisfactory diagnostic techniques and such therapeutic measures as are indicated in specific disorders. In addition, osteopathic principles and practice are interrelated early in the basic science program and coordinated with basic teachings in the first and second years.

The first year is heavily weighted in general courses in anatomy (including histology, embryology, and osteology), biochemistry (including nutrition), genetics, immunology, microbiology, pathology (general), pharmacology (general), physiology, and osteopathic principles and practice. Each of these disciplines is presented in a basic, clinically oriented fashion, providing elemental preclinical medical information. Building on the knowledge of the basic sciences gained in the first year, the curriculum becomes progressively more clinical with the study of the neuromuscular, musculoskeletal, cardiovascular, respiratory, gastrointestinal, endocrine, and renal systems. Other courses designed to prepare the student physician for clinical patient exposure include community medicine, dermatology, geriatrics, medical jurisprudence, pediatrics, psychiatry, rheumatology, toxicology, and surgical subspecialties. During the second year, students rotate through NYCOM's on-campus Family Health Care Center to attain exposure in performing patient history and physical examinations. The next two years are devoted to clinical clerkships with mandatory rotations in the following services: medicine, surgery, family practice, obstetrics/gynecology, pediatrics, and psychiatry. Specialty areas are also covered. Training in the clinical sciences takes place at NYCOM operated Family Health Care Centers, and an extensive network of affiliated hospitals.

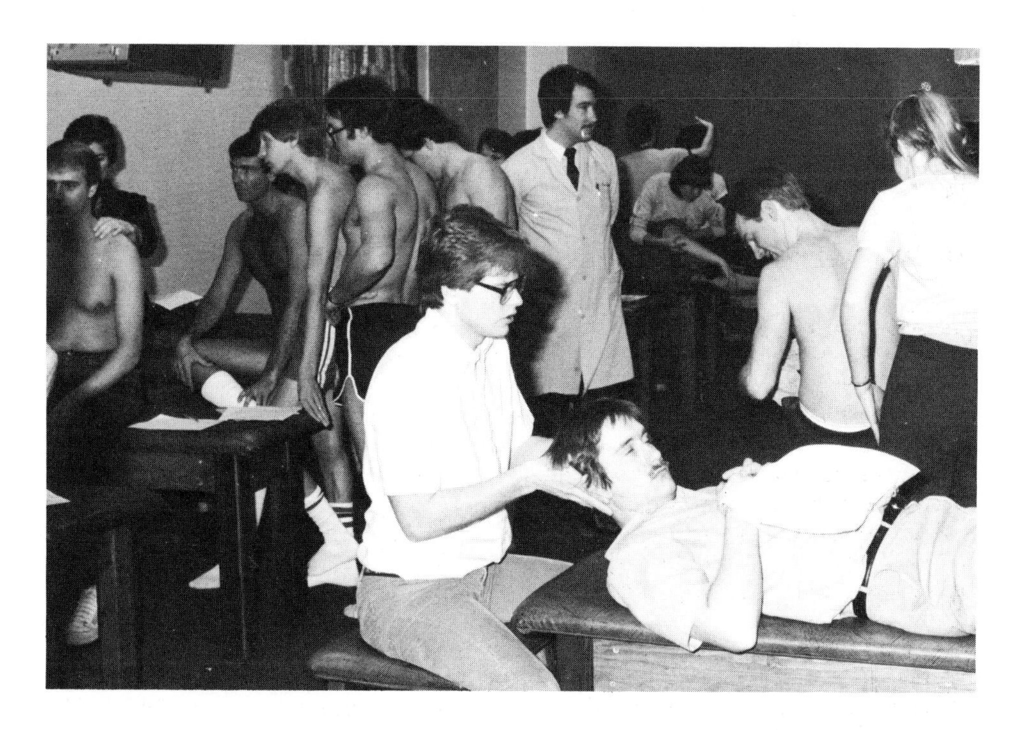

Student Applicants: In assessing a candidate for admission, both cognitive and non-cognitive factors are considered including academic excellence, interpersonal skills, and knowledge and interest in osteopathic medicine. Out-of-state applicants should be aware that only a limited number of non-residents are accepted.

As an outgrowth of NYCOM's Affirmative Action Program, the Office of Minority Affairs was established to strengthen the college's capability in the recruitment and subsequent enrollment of students from underrepresented minority groups.

The Director of Minority Affairs actively engages in activities to identify qualified applicants including conducting outreach programs to enhance visibility of the osteopathic profession and NYCOM with respect to area high schools, colleges, community agencies, and minority health professional organizations. NYCOM also conducts an on-campus Osteopathic Awareness Program during the month of June for qualified premed students within the college's geographic area. This program offers mini-courses in the basic sciences, study skills, clinical exposure, and an introduction to osteopathic medicine. It has proven to be an effective method of recruiting underrepresented minority candidates.

Once enrolled, minority student-physicians are provided with moral support, culturally sensitive counseling services, tutorials where indicated, assistance with financial aid, and appropriate referrals. These activities have generated positive results and a data base for expansion of the Minority Affairs Program.

Interested minority students are encouraged to contact the Office of Minority Affairs for additional information and assistance.

Entrance Requirements:

- A minimum science grade point averge of 2.5 on a 4.0 scale and an overall grade point average of 2.75 on a 4.0 scale.

- A baccalaureate degree or at least 90 semester hours (30 of which must be on the baccalaureate level) in an accredited college or university.

- Each applicant must submit New Medical College Admission Test (MCAT) scores. Applicants should take the examination in the spring of the junior year or no later than the fall of the senior year.

- Applicants must have completed an acceptable academic year sequence (generally eight semester hours) with no grade below a 2.0 on a 4.0 scale in each of the following subjects: English (composition preferable); biology (including a basic course in general biology or general zoology, including two semester hours of laboratory); general chemistry (lecture and laboratory); organic chemistry (including the study of aliphatic and aromatic compounds, including two semester hours of laboratory); and physics (including the study of mechanics, sound, heat, magnetism, electricity and light, including two semester hours of laboratory).

The above are minimum requirements for admission to NYCOM. Students are urged to enroll in additional courses such as English, calculus, comparative anatomy, genetics, physical chemistry, quantitative analytical chemistry, and behavioral sciences. The potential applicant should complete these requirements as early as possible.

Admissions Process: Upon receipt of the completed application and required credentials, those who are interviewed will be so notified. An applicant must be interviewed prior to consideration by the Committee on Admission for acceptance. A request to appear for an interview should not be construed as an offer of acceptance. The New York College of Osteopathic Medicine issues acceptances on a rolling basis. Upon filling the class, an alternate list is formulated and applicants are notified as openings become available. In 1985, the size of the entering class was 130 students.

Application Deadline: The annual application deadline is December 1. Applications are filed through AACOMAS.

Tuition: $12,500 (Tuition is subject to change).

Total Enrollment 1984-1985: 465

Minority Applicant/Admissions Statistics:

	1984-1985			
	Black Americans	American Indians/ American Natives	Hispanics	Asian Americans/ Pacific Islanders
First Year Enrolled	4	0	4	5
Total Enrolled	6	0	10	12

Principal Contacts:

Philip F. Fleisher, D.O., Dean and Provost for Medical Affairs
Michael J. Schaefer, Director of Admissions
Sharon E. Moore, M.S.W., Director of Student and Minority Affairs

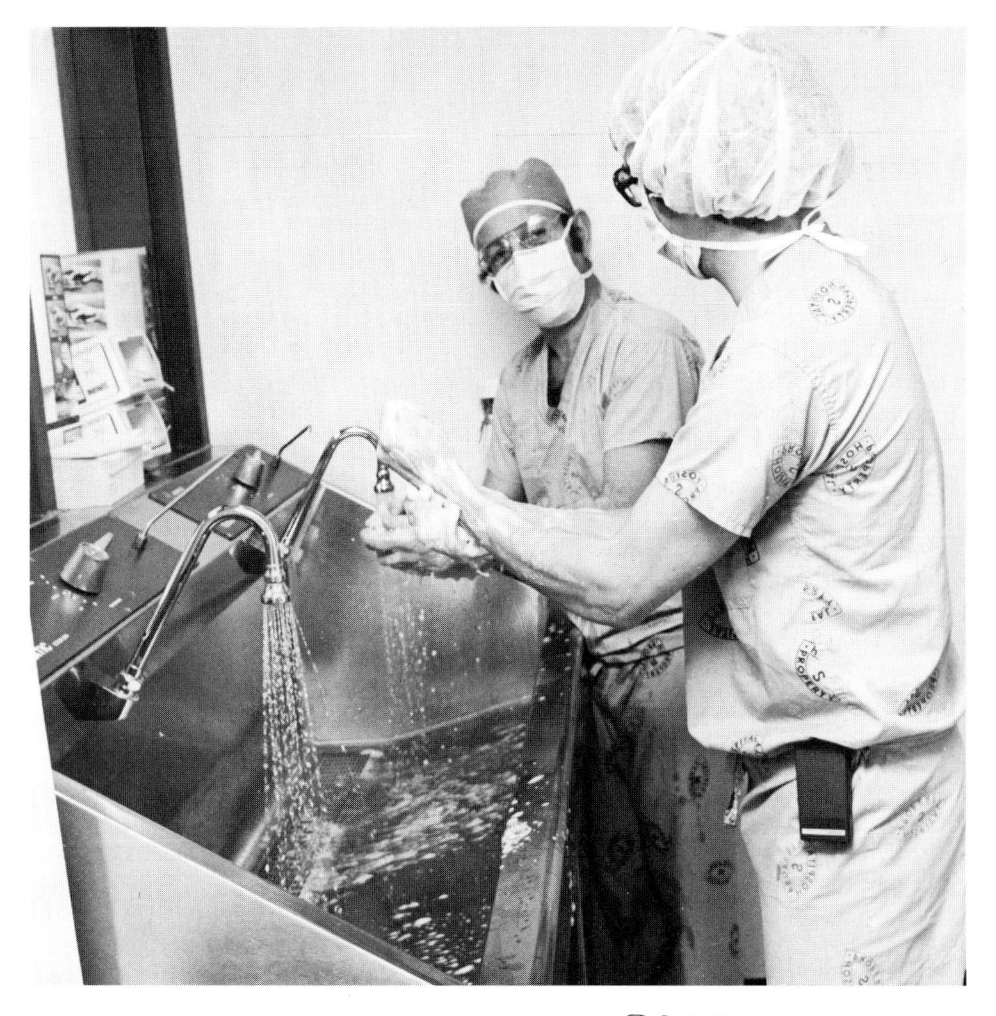

Ohio University College of Osteopathic Medicine

Grosvenor, Irvine, and Parks Halls
Athens, Ohio 45701
Telephone: (614) 594-6401

Year Founded: 1975

Status: Public, State Supported

Background: Established by act of the Ohio General Assembly in 1975, the College of Osteopathic Medicine was created to help alleviate the state's growing shortage of family physicians and to train doctors for chronically underserved areas. Every facet of the curriculum, therefore, is organized to give students maximum exposure to family practice. For instance, the college has developed, in conjunction with other agencies and several Southeastern Ohio communities, a network of rural medical clinics. In these facilities, students become acquainted with rural practice and, at the same time, provide needed health care to the underserved Appalachian part of the state in which Ohio University is located.

The college has been steadily expanding physical facilities both on the main campus in Athens, and at the seven Regional Teaching Centers across the state. Facilities specifically for Ohio University students have been built at Doctors Hospital of Columbus and at Youngstown Osteopathic Hospital. The General Assembly has approved funds for construction of teaching facilities at Grandview Hospital in Dayton as part of the state's 1984-86 capital improvement budget. All of these new facilities help the College of Osteopathic Medicine offer increased educational opportunities to osteopathic medical students.

The curriculum of the Ohio University College of Osteopathic Medicine (OUCOM) is based upon the expanding spiral approach. A key to this design is that as the basis of student knowledge expands, he or she is presented with medical subject matter in such a way that an increasingly sharpened focus is drawn on how such material relates to the practice of a primary care physician. Each segment of the curriculum, called a phase, is designed to integrate the clinical and basic science aspects of medicine with emphasis on the basic sciences at the beginning and on the clinical sciences near the end. To accomplish this integration, faculty in both areas must cross disciplinary boundaries and work together to provide students with a maximum understanding of the important interrelationships in biology and medicine.

In addition to the Doctor of Osteopathy (D.O.) program, the school also offers a special degree program of D.O./Ph.D. An extensive research program has been established. Two areas of special emphasis are genetics and somatic dysfunction.

Student Applicants: Preference is given to residents of the State of Ohio and more than 80 percent of each class have been Ohio residents. Among non-resident candidates, priority of consideration is given to individuals who show promise of making unique contributions to the profession and who agree to practice in Ohio for at least five years following completion of their medical training. Applications for admission are evaluated on the basis of scholarship, personal fitness, motivation for osteopathic medicine, and dedication to the humane delivery of quality medical care. The school believes that other factors besides grade point average are critical in the selection of students. Hence, after the determination of academic ability to perform well, these other factors will assume major importance.

Entrance Requirements:

- In-state residents — A minimum grade point average of 2.5 on a 4.0 scale in both science and non-science areas. Out-of-state male applicants should have at least a 3.25 grade point average, out-of-state female applicants should have a 3.00, and out-of-state minority applicants should have a 2.50 grade point average; all on a 4.0 scale in both the science and non-science areas.

- Four year baccalaureate degree from a regionally accredited college or university.

- New Medical College Admission Test to be taken no later than the fall of the application year.

- One academic year in each of the following with a grade no lower than 2.0 on a 4.0 scale: general chemistry, organic chemistry, biology and physics (usually 8 semester hours or 12 quarter hours), behavioral sciences and English (usually 6 semester hours or 9 quarter hours).

Admissions Process: Admissions to a class are determined from interviews held between October 15 and March 1. As candidates are interviewed, seats are filled and candidates are notified. Interviews are granted only upon invitation and only after the receipt of all materials requested. Applicants are encouraged to apply early to receive consideration. The size of the 1984 entering class was 100 students.

Application Deadline: The annual application deadline is December 1. Applications are filed through AACOMAS.

Tuition: Residents, $4,605; non-residents, $6,546. (Tuition is subject to change.)

Total Enrollment 1984-1985: 354

Minority Applicant/Admissions Statistics:

	1983-1984			
	Black Americans	American Indians/ American Natives	Hispanics	Asian Americans/ Pacific Islanders
First Year Enrolled	6	1	0	3
Total Enrolled	10	1	6	9

Principal Contacts:

Frank W. Myers, D.O., Dean
John Molea, D.O., Associate Dean for Academic and Clinical Affairs
James P. Artis, Ph.D., Assistant Dean for Student Programs

The Oklahoma College of Osteopathic Medicine and Surgery

1111 West 17th Street
Tulsa, Oklahoma 74107
Telephone: (918) 582-1972

Year Founded: 1972

Status: Public, State Supported

Background: The Oklahoma College of Osteopathic Medicine and Surgery was established as the first free-standing, state-supported osteopathic medical college in the nation. In 1977, the college moved into a permanent campus complex on the west bank of the Arkansas River.

The four-year program uses a coordinated, spiraling systems approach. In a spiral curriculum, subject matter is continuously reintroduced in greater depth and complexity. This serves to reinforce learning and promote meaningful retention.

The first year is designed to bring students to the desired level of knowledge in the basic sciences and provide preliminary clinical knowledge. The second and third years emphasize the interdisciplinary study of the structure, function, and clinical procedures associated with selected body systems. The final year of the program is predominately clinically-oriented and community-based, and consists of clerkship experiences in hospitals and clinics where students observe patients under physician-faculty supervision. During half of the final year the student rotates through basic hospital services including surgery, obstetrics/gynecology, pediatrics, internal medicine, and emergency room. The balance of the clinical-study year consists of supervised patient contact in small towns and rural areas throughout Oklahoma. The student spends a few weeks at each of several locations including a small rural hospital, primary care clinic, Junior Partnership, community health facility, psychiatric facility, and one elective location.

Student Applicants: The college considers applications for admission from all qualified candidates without regard to age, sex, creed, race, or national origin. Strong preference is given to Oklahoma residents. Those residents who have experienced unequal educational opportunities for social, cultural or racial reasons, are particularly urged to

apply. Applicants must be American citizens or have obtained "permanent resident" status to be considered. The size of the 1984 entering class was 88 students.

Entrance Requirements:

- A minimum grade point average of 2.5 on a 4.0 scale for science subjects and overall.

- A minimum of three years of undergraduate study and not less than 75 percent of the prescribed requirements for a baccalaureate degree at an accredited college or university.

- Results of the New Medical College Admission Test (MCAT) must be submitted. Applicants are encouraged to take the examination in the spring preceding the admission date.

- Applicants must have completed by the time of enrollment, an acceptable full academic year sequence with no grade below 2.0 on a 4.0 scale in each of the following subjects: English, biology, inorganic chemistry, organic chemistry, and physics.

Admissions Process: Applicants who are invited for a personal interview must participate to qualify for further consideration. Interview results will be considered along with the other data submitted in determining which applicants have demonstrated appropriate levels of scholarship, aptitude, and motivation for admission to the program.

Application Deadline: The annual application deadline is November 1. Applications are filed through AACOMAS.

Tuition: In-state residents, $2,435; Out-of-state residents, $5,343. (Tuition is subject to change.)

Total Enrollment 1984-1985: 340

Minority Applicant/Admissions Statistics: Unavailable

Principal Contacts:

Rodney T. Houlihan, Ph.D., Acting President
Jack R. Wolfe, D.O., Dean of Academic Affairs
Frank Hohengarten, Ed.D., Director of Student Services and Registrar

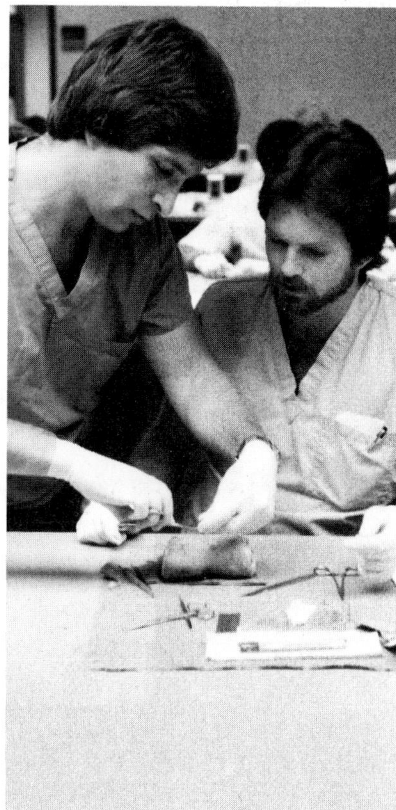

Philadelphia College of Osteopathic Medicine

4150 City Avenue
Philadelphia, Pennsylvania 19131
Telephone: (215) 581-6000

Year Founded: 1899

Status: Private

Background: Philadelphia College of Osteopathic Medicine is the largest of the U.S. osteopathic medical colleges and has graduated over 6,000 physicians since its inception. The College, located twenty minutes from Philadelphia's historic center, forms the core of The Osteopathic Medical Center of Philadelphia. The Center includes the 212-bed F. H. Barth Pavilion Hospital; Moss House that houses administrative offices; Evans Hall which is a seven-story classroom, library, laboratory, and research building; a School of Allied Health; and Rowland Hall which houses classrooms, physicians' offices, study area, a 500-seat lecture hall, student activities area, bookstore, and other offices.

The four-year curriculum is comprehensive. It has as its goal the preparation of the student for the general practice of osteopathic medicine. Throughout the course of studies, the principles and practice of the osteopathic technique are applied in specific fields. The first two years of the instruction program are oriented toward study of the basic sciences, anatomy, physiology, histology, biochemistry, microbiology, and other similar courses. Additional study is provided in osteopathic principles and practices, internal medicine, surgery, neurology, psychiatry, physical diagnosis, and radiology. The third and fourth years emphasize clinical experience under physician supervision with selected advanced study in the basic sciences.

Student Applicants: The college, following its long-standing tradition, welcomes qualified students of both sexes, from all racial, religious, and socio-economic backgrounds. Applicants for admission are evaluated on the basis of their scholarship, extracurricular activities, community and volunteer service, integrity, dedication, and motivation for the study of osteopathic medicine. Preference is given to residents of Pennsylvania and neighboring states. The college is committed to increasing its accessibility to minority and disadvantaged students, through special admissions and academic counseling, the high school Osteopathic Discovery Program, minority college recruiting, financial assistance, and the Summer-Start Preparation Program. The size of the 1984 entering class was 215 students.

Entrance Requirements:

- A bachelor's degree from an accredited college or university.

- One academic year of each of the following, including laboratory: inorganic chemistry, organic chemistry, biology, and physics. One academic year of English and mathematics.

- Each applicant must submit scores from the Medical College Admission Test. Applicants are urged to take the examination in the spring of their junior year, but definitely no later than the fall of their senior year.

Admissions Process: Upon receipt of the completed application and required credentials, the Faculty Committee on Admissions will select those applicants to be interviewed. All applicants who are eventually accepted must be interviewed. A request to appear for an interview should not be construed by the applicant as evidence of final acceptance.

Applicant Deadline: The annual application deadline date is December 1. Applications must be filed directly with the College.

Tuition: In-state residents, $11,250; Out-of-state residents, $11,550. (Tuition subject to change.)

Total Enrollment 1984-1985: 833

Minority Applicant/Admissions Statistics: Unavailable

Principal Contacts:

J. Peter Tilley, D.O., President
Joseph Dieterle, D.O., Dean
Carol A. Fox, Director of Admissions and Student Affairs

Southeastern College of Osteopathic Medicine

1750 N.E. 168th Street
North Miami Beach, Florida 33162
Telephone: (305) 949-4000

Year Founded: 1979

Status: Private, non-profit institution

Background The Southeastern College of Osteopathic Medicine is located in a metropolitan area which offers a wide selection of cultural, educational, and recreational activities. The area is served by public transportation and is accessible from several major highways and two international airports — Miami and Fort Lauderdale. The college complex occupies most of a city block and is adjacent to the Southeastern Medical Center, an affiliated osteopathic teaching hospital. Located in a quiet residential neighborhood, the campus includes the three-level John F. Hull Administration Building, a new and ultra-modern Education Building, and several small structures. A new building is scheduled for completion in 1986.

Southeastern College of Osteopathic Medicine's four-year curriculum leading to the Doctor of Osteopathy degree has as its goal the preparation of the student for the general practice of osteopathic medicine. The curriculum is divided into several phases. The first five semesters are spent on campus and include the basic sciences and didactic clinical sciences. During this part of their training, students also are introduced to patient evaluation and the technology of medicine, and special emphasis is placed on osteopathic principles and practice. In the second phase, students spend seventeen months in clinical training, including teaching rotations in affiliated hospitals and experience in ambulatory care facilities. Nearly 1,700 teaching beds are provided by osteopathic hospitals in Florida and in Georgia. Students then return to campus for a two-month eighth semester featuring basic/clinical science correlations and preparation for internship, residency, and practice. The curriculum emphasizes general practice and features training in ambulatory care, geriatrics, rural medicine, minority medicine, medical communications, and humanities.

Student Applicants: An interview by the Committee on Admissions is granted to selected students. Selection factors considered include evidence of interest in and knowledge of osteopathic medicine, leadership qualities, and community activity in health care and other fields. The school seeks qualified, mature, and well-motivated students, primarily from Florida and neighboring southeastern states who will be able to serve the health care needs of this region as osteopathic physicians. Applicants must be citizens of the United States or have obtained a "permanent resident" status to be considered. The Southeastern College of Osteopathic Medicine does not discriminate on the basis of age, race, color, religion, sex, or handicap in the administration of all college-related programs. The size of the 1985 entering class was 100 students.

Entrance Requirements:

- A bachelor's degree from an accredited college or university.
- Each applicant must submit scores from the New Medical College Admission Test taken within two years of application to the college. It is *strongly recommended* that the New Medical College Admission Test be taken in the spring of the year preceding the admission date.
- One academic year of each of the following, including laboratory: inorganic chemistry, organic chemistry, biology, and physics. One academic year of English composition and literature. Students are urged to enroll in additional courses in the behavioral sciences, cultural subjects, and in the humanities. Embryology and genetics are also suggested.

Admissions Process: Upon receipt of the completed application and required credentials, the Committee on Admissions will select those who are to be interviewed. All applicants who are accepted must be interviewed, but an invitation to appear for an interview should not be construed by the applicant as evidence of final acceptance. Notices of acceptance or other action by the Committee on Admissions will be on a "rolling" or periodic schedule.

Application Deadline: The annual application deadline is January 1. Applications are filed through AACOMAS.

Tuition: In-state residents and Mississippi students who qualify under the SREB program, $11,500; Out-of-state residents, $15,550. (Tuition is subject to change.)

Total Enrollment 1984-1985: 273

Minority Applicant/Admissions Statistics:

	1984-1985			
	Black Americans	American Indians/ American Natives	Hispanics	Asian Americans/ Pacific Islanders
First Year Enrolled	1	1	8	1
Total Enrolled	4	2	11	2

Principal Contacts:

Morton Terry, D.O., President
Arnold Melnick, D.O., Dean
Marla Frohlinger, Director of Admissions and Student Affairs

Texas College of Osteopathic Medicine

Camp Bowie at Montgomery
Fort Worth, Texas 76107
Telephone: (817) 735-2000

Year Founded: 1966

Status: Public, State Supported

Background: Chartered in 1966 as a privately funded institution, the Texas College of Osteopathic Medicine (TCOM) by legislative act in 1975, became a state institution under direction of the Board of Regents of North Texas State University. The school is centered in a growing osteopathic medical area which includes Fort Worth Osteopathic Hospital, cultural complexes and medical centers.

In 1980, the Texas College of Osteopathic Medicine became the first medical school in the country to commit itself to a curriculum built around the promotion of health. The college adopted a statement of educational goals outlining a plan for changing the emphasis in education of future physicians from "defensive" treatment of disease to "offensive" promotion of health. While recognizing its obligation to train students to attack existing disease in the traditional manner, the college concentrates equally on training future physicians to promote health and wellness among their patients. The school searches for students whose personal philosophies are compatible with its goals.

The curriculum stresses the care of patients in the context of a wide variety of factors that affect the health of the patient such as economic status, occupation, and environment. Emphasis is also placed on promoting and maintaining the health of the patient at the highest level possible through planning with the patient for diet, exercise and other healthful elements.

Semesters 1 and 2 of the first year are devoted primarily to instruction in the pre-clinical sciences. However, during the same period, an introduction is made to the clinical sciences through the departments of general and family practice and osteopathic philosophy, principles, and practice. The following three terms, Semesters 3-5, are periods of study increasingly devoted to didactic instruction in the clinical sciences in preparation for the clinical clerkship rotations and preceptorships that follow. The final months of the curriculum are devoted to clinical clerkship rotations, preceptorship assignments, and further studies in both pre-clinical and clinical sciences. During Semesters 6, 7, and 8, each student rotates through a series of preceptorships, clinic and hospital clerkships for a 15-

month period. These rotations, units of four weeks each, are scheduled primarily in physicians' offices, college clinics, and teaching hospitals of the college located in or near the Fort Worth-Dallas area. Semester 8 also includes additional clinical and classroom activities designed to round out the students' preparation for graduation. During this final semester each student attends a specially designed program of short courses and clinical seminars on campus. Topics addressed in this program are selected according to the educational needs of the student as determined in the months prior to graduation.

Student Applicants: The State of Texas Legislative Appropriation requires that a minimum of 90 percent of each entering class be Texas residents. In assessing applicants, the college attempts to evaluate the whole person. Although selection utilizes the standard academic criteria (grade point average, the New Medical College Admission Test scores), the college believes that the following factors are also critical in the selection of students: work experience and work load while in college; life experiences, that is, health-related experience and/or people-oriented experiences; extracurricular activities; potential to contribute to the quality of the entering class; recommendations and motivation for osteopathic medicine. All qualified applicants will be considered for admission without regard to handicap, sex, ethnic, social, or cultural backgrounds. The college actively seeks minority students and offers programs to facilitate enrollment and academic progress. Academic enrichment courses, special tutoring, counseling, and financial aid are available if needed.

Entrance Requirements:

- In-state residents: A minimum preprofessional science grade point average of at least 2.5 on a 4.0 scale, and an overall grade point average of at least 2.5. Out-of-state residents with less than a 3.0 overall grade point average are not encouraged to apply. It should be noted that the average grade point for the previous entering classes has been well above a 3.0 on a 4.0 scale.
- A minimum of 3 years (90 semester hours) of undergraduate credit from an accredited college or university; 99 percent of selected applicants have earned a B.S. or B.A. degree by the time they matriculate into the Texas College of Osteopathic Medicine.
- The New Medical College Admission Test can be no older than 3 years and should be taken no later than the fall of the year preceding that for which an application is made.
- Minimum course requirements: A full academic year of the following, each with laboratory: biological sciences, general chemistry, organic chemistry, and physics. In addition, one academic year of English and behavioral sciences. Additional coursework in the traditional basic sciences, the humanities, and behavioral sciences is encouraged. Also, the following courses are highly recommended, not so much for application purposes as for survival in the medical school curriculum: biochemistry, comparative anatomy, embryology, genetics, physiology, and microbiology.

Admissions Process: Following a review of the applications, those applicants whose credentials are found to be satisfactory according to the guidelines set forth by the Admissions Committee will be invited for a personal interview from September 15 through February. The interviewers have been charged to assess the following: osteopathic motivation, problem solving skills, and ethical decision making skills. Based upon the recommendations of the Admission Committee, the President of the school makes the final decision. As decisions are made, candidates are notified. The size of the 1984 entering class was 100 students.

Tuition: In-state residents, $1,219; Out-of-state residents, $4,876. (Tuition is subject to change.)

Total Enrollment 1984-1985: 395

Minority Applicant/Admissions Statistics:

	1983-1984			
	Black Americans	American Indians/ American Natives	Hispanics	Asian Americans/ Pacific Islanders
Applied	39	16	44	57
First Year Enrolled	5	3	11	4
Total Enrolled	4	3	11	4

Principal Contacts:

David M. Richards, D.O., Acting President
T. Eugene Zachary, D.O., Acting Vice President for Academic Affairs and Dean
Richard Sinclair, Ph.D., Acting Director of Admissions

The University of Health Sciences/ College of Osteopathic Medicine

2105 Independence Boulevard
Kansas City, Missouri 64124
Telephone: (816) 283-2000

Year Founded: 1916

Status: Private

Background: The University of Health Sciences/College of Osteopathic Medicine is located on a 35-acre campus two miles northeast of downtown Kansas City, Missouri. The College operates two teaching hospitals and a skilled nursing facility. The University Hospital is a ten-level structure situated on the university campus. Completed in 1973, it accommodates 426 private patient rooms and incorporates teaching and patient care facilities which are among the most advanced in the United States.

The primary objective of the college is to promote the study and theory of the practice of osteopathic medicine. Emphasis is placed on clinical training in family medicine, internal medicine, pediatrics, obstetrics, gynecology, emergency medicine, and surgery, with primary care being emphasized in the third and fourth years of clinical instruction. Within the scope of the educational program, the college presents the basic concepts of scientific medicine, emphasizing the tenets and principles essential to the practice of osteopathic medicine. The courses of instruction are organized under 16 departments. The curriculum is taught over a period of four calendar years. The first two and one-half years of instruction consist of didactic experience. Clinical rotations are done in the second semester of the third year. The fourth year consists of clerkships. Preceptorship training in family medicine with a physician located in a rural area is an integral part of the fourth-year educational program.

Student Applicants: Applicants are considered on their intellectual ability, superior scholastic achievement, commitment, and suitability to succeed in the study and practice of osteopathic medicine. All applicants are considered for entry into the first-year class irrespective of advanced degrees or specialized training. University policies are non-discriminatory. The size of the 1984 entering class was 160 students.

Entrance Requirements:

- Four years of study and receipt of the baccalaureate degree or equivalent from an accredited college or university.

- The minimum course requirements are one academic year of each of the following, including laboratory: organic chemistry (aliphatic and aromatic compounds) and college physics; twelve semester hours of general biology (including a separate course in embryology); and one academic year of English composition and literature. Applicants are strongly advised to provide evidence of a solid foundation and demonstrated proficiency in the biological and physical sciences. They are expected to have studied comparative vertebrate anatomy, genetics, analytical chemistry, and mathematics.

- The New Medical College Admissions Test is required.

Admissions Process: Academic excellence and non-academic achievements are the major criteria on which applicants are rated. Based on the initial assessment, selected applicants are invited to visit the campus for an interview. Subsequent to the interview, the Committee on Admissions reviews all information and applicants are notified as soon as a final admissions decision is made.

Applicant Deadline: The annual application deadline is December 1. Applications must be filed directly with the College.

Tuition: $12,350 (Tuition is subject to change).

Total Enrollment 1983-1984: 610

Minority Applicant/Admissions Statistics: Unavailable

Principal Contacts:

Rudolph S. Bremen, Ph.D., President
Leonard Mennen, D.O., Dean
Winifred W. Massad, Ph.D., Assistant Dean

University of Osteopathic Medicine and Health Sciences

3200 Grand Avenue
Des Moines, Iowa 50312
Telephone: (515) 271-1400

Year Founded: 1898

Status: Private

Background: In December 1980, the Board of Trustees of the College of Osteopathic Medicine and Surgery (COMS) voted to become the University of Osteopathic Medicine and Health Sciences by the addition of a program in Podiatric Medicine and a program leading to a Bachelor of Science degree and a Physician's Assistant diploma. While the core of the University's programs remains osteopathic medicine, the addition of these programs led to the creation of a health sciences university.

Within the University is the College of Osteopathic Medicine and Surgery, which offers a four-year program of medical study leading to the Doctor of Osteopathy degree (D.O.). The osteopathic medical curriculum stresses the holistic approach to man and his health problems. It is oriented to a clinical emphasis from the very outset of a student's career and stresses that man is an integrated organism incorporating a number of functioning systems. Thus, the College of Osteopathic Medicine and Surgery has developed a highly integrated, systems-approach medical curriculum reflecting the interrelationship and interdependence of the body systems. For the major part of the first year, students will take core courses in the basic sciences. This is followed by the study of pre-clinical and clinical medicine using an integrated organ system approach. The last half of the third year and the entire fourth year are devoted to clinical clerkships in hospitals and outpatient clinics in family practice, medicine, surgery, pediatrics, obstetrics, gynecology, and psychiatry. Medical history and physical diagnosis are introduced in the first year of the curriculum as are the principles, practices, and theory of osteopathic manipulative medicine which are taught during the entire academic curriculum.

The college maintains and operates ten teaching clinics within a 35-mile radius of Des Moines and has affiliations with several other family practice clinics located in Iowa and throughout the nation. Teaching programs have been established with 12 hospitals throughout the profession.

Student Applicants: The college seeks to enroll mature men and women who have the motivation and ability to develop into competent and compassionate osteopathic physicians. The school actively recruits disadvantaged and minority candidates who are strongly motivated to pursue careers in medicine. Such candidates must demonstrate the personal qualities necessary to successfully prepare for a career in osteopathic medicine. Motivation, desire and interest are weighed in evaluating disadvantaged and minority students. The college also assists disadvantaged students through academic tutoring as needed.

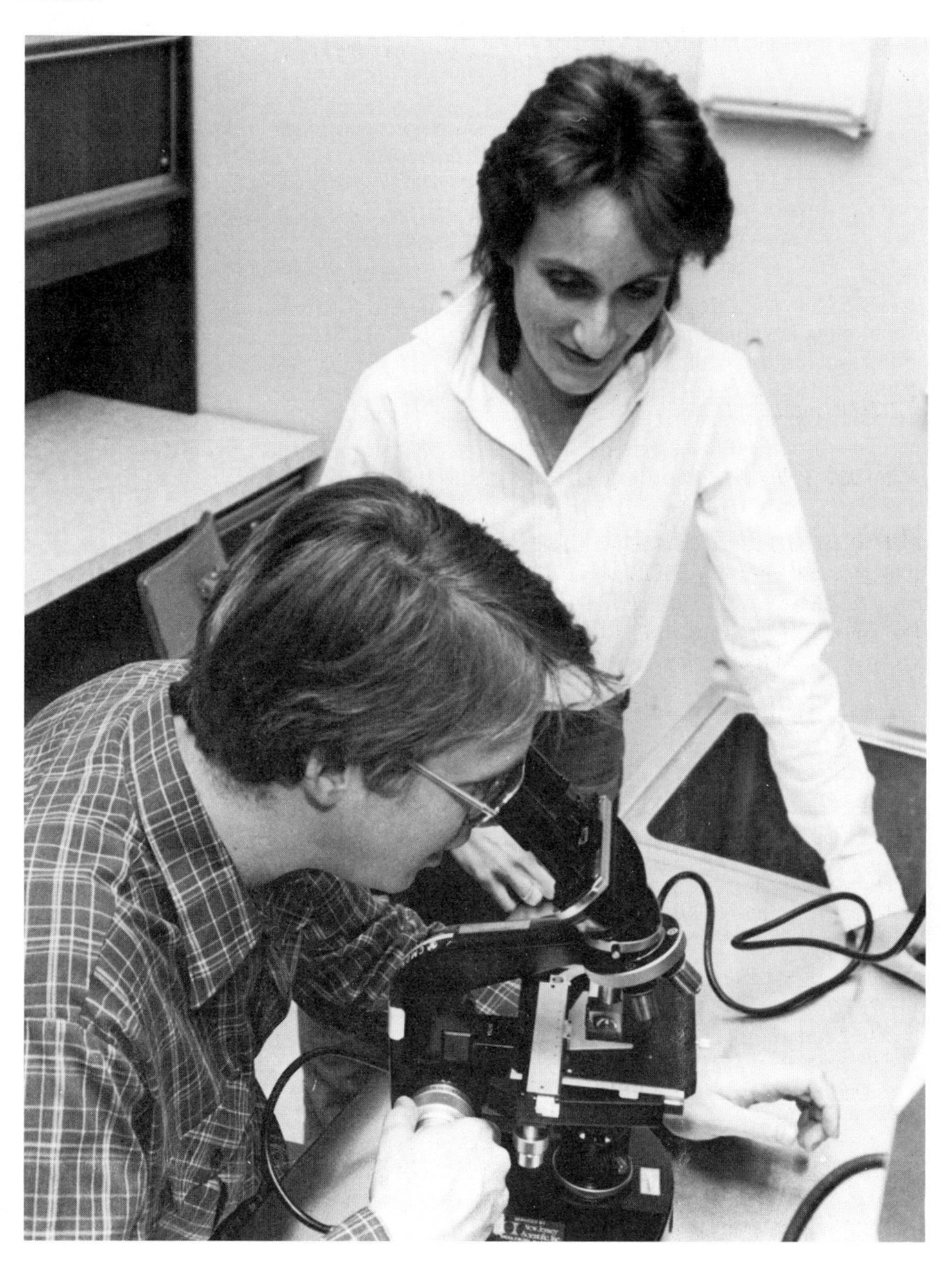

Entrance Requirements:

- A minimum grade point average of 2.5 on a 4.0 scale and a 2.0 on a 4.0 scale science grade point average.
- Although a baccalaureate degree is strongly preferred, exceptional candidates may be accepted upon completion of 75 percent of undergraduate degree work.
- All applicants must take the New Medical College Admission Test. It is strongly recommended that this test be taken in the spring of the year preceding the admission date. However, the September date is acceptable.
- All candidates must complete one academic year of the following requirements with a grade of "C" or higher: English composition and rhetoric; general chemistry with laboratory; organic chemistry with laboratory; biology with laboratory; physics with laboratory. Recommended are courses in English literature, biochemistry, genetics, comparative anatomy, mathematics, and psychology.

Admissions Process: The Admissions Committee will invite selected applicants to Des Moines for a personal interview. Selection factors include demonstrated academic ability (including Medical College Admission Test scores), leadership and community service, and letters of reference. The personal interview is given great weight in making the final admissions decision. Candidates are expected to have taken the initiative to become familiar with the philosophy and practice of osteopathic medicine. Candidates not invited for interview will be so notified. The size of the 1984 entering class was 180 students.

Application Deadline: The annual application deadline is December 1. Applications are filed through AACOMAS.

Tuition: $12,775 (Tuition is subject to change).

Total Enrollment 1984-1985: 720

Minority Applicant/Admissions Statistics:

	1983-1984			
	Black Americans	American Indians/ American Natives	Hispanics	Asian Americans/ Pacific Islanders
First Year Enrolled	1	0	0	6
Total Enrolled	4	0	4	12

Principal Contacts:

J. Leonard Azneer, Ph.D., President
Joseph H. Walsh, Ph.D., D.O., Dean for Academic Affairs
Dennis Bates, Ph.D., Director of Admissions

West Virginia School of Osteopathic Medicine

400 North Lee Street
Lewisburg, West Virginia 24901
Telephone: (304) 645-6270

Year Founded: 1972

Status: Public, State Supported

Background: Chartered in 1972 as the private Greenbrier College of Osteopathic Medicine, the West Virginia School of Osteopathic Medicine (WVSOM) became a unit of the West Virginia State System of Higher Education early in 1976.

Greenbrier County was chosen because of its strategic location in rural Appalachia. Lewisburg, with a population of 5,000, is the third oldest town in West Virginia. Located high in the heart of the scenic Appalachian Mountain range, the surrounding Greenbrier Valley is noted for its beauty, magnificent farmlands and bluegrass pasture lands in the foothills of the Allegheny Mountains, where summits reach 5,000 feet. With its unique blend of nearby historical sites, farmlands, coal and timber industries, wilderness areas, and modern resorts, the Greenbrier Valley is truly diverse in nature.

The 43-acre campus has a large main building complete with classrooms, auditorium, library, laboratory areas, administrative and faculty offices. One wing consists of a modern diagnostic and out-patient clinic. Other facilities include animal care facilities, student union and numerous athletic facilities for students.

The emphasis of the program is to prepare osteopathic medical students who are motivated to practice family medicine in rural areas. Consequently, the curriculum is designed to produce physicians who are competent in rural practice settings while assuring that they will have the educational competence and legal status required for licensure in all states. The first year includes courses in the basic biomedical sciences that provide the foundation for the study of the organ systems that follow. The study of anatomy is emphasized in the first year, as well as fundamental courses in other basic biomedical disciplines and osteopathic principles and practice. In addition, the first year includes courses that are especially important in WVSOM's mission of training general practitioners for West Virginia; these include nutrition, preventive medicine, and occupational medicine. During the second year and the first term of the third year, preclinical and clinical instruction is arranged to deal with one organ system at a time. Training in osteopathic principles and practice continues throughout this phase of the curriculum. The osteopathic

concepts of the integrity of the body, the interrelationships of structure and function, and the role of the musculoskeletal system in health and disease pervade the entire four-year curriculum. Students spend two months of the summer following the second year with preceptors. Introduction to the clinical aspects of pre-clinical sciences occurs early in the student's career, in the correlated organs systems instruction. Limited clinical training is conducted during the pre-clinical years. Under the supervision of physicians at the Campus Health Center, nearby hospitals, rural clinics, nursing homes and public health sites, students learn practical clinical procedures. Concentrated clinical training is initiated in the third year and continues until graduation.

Student Applicants: First preference is given to West Virginia residents who comprise about 80 percent of each class. West Virginia School of Osteopathic Medicine participates in a contractual agreement through the Southern Regional Educational Board (SREB), in which the school may award class seats and gives preference to Maryland, Georgia and Mississippi residents. Students selected under this program will be subject to the same tuition and fees as in-state students. Applicants may contact the Admissions Office for information and/or addresses of their state agencies for program eligibility. It is the responsibility of the applicant to verify eligibility for the Southern Regional Educational Board program. Other preference is given to residents of Applachian states, particularly in the southeastern section of the United States. All applicants must participate in the regular application process.

Entrance Requirements:

- A grade point average of at least 2.5 in sciences on a 4.0 scale. Applicants should be aware that the average science grade point average for previous entering classes has been better than a 3.0.

- 90 semester hours or three-fourths of the credits required for a baccalaureate degree from an accredited college or university. The majority of candidates accepted for admission will have completed four or more years of preprofessional study.

- New Medical College Admission Test (MCAT) is required. It should be taken no later than the fall of the calendar year preceding that for which matriculation is desired.

- Course requirements include a minimum of one academic year of each of the following: English, general biology or zoology, physics, inorganic chemistry and organic chemistry. It is expected that labs will be included in each of the basic sciences. It is strongly recommended that prospective applicants take one or two additional courses in the following categories: molecular biology, organismic biology, and liberal arts.

Admissions Process: The committee on Admissions has the responsibility of accepting applicants on the basis of aptitude, maturity, motivation for osteopathic medicine, personal fitness, and scholarship. Hobbies, letters of recommendation, outside activities, and scholarship are all evaluated to aid in the selection process. A personal interview granted by the Admissions Committee is required before acceptance is considered. First preference is given to residents of West Virginia and to residents of SREB states. In 1983 the size of the entering class was 68 students.

Application Deadline: The annual application deadline is December 1. Applications are filed through AACOMAS.

Tuition: Residents, $1,892; Non-residents, $4,512. (Tuition is subject to change.)

Total Enrollment 1984-1985: 235

Minority Applicant/Admissions Statistics:

	1982-1983			
	Black Americans	American Indians/ American Natives	Hispanics	Asian Americans/ Pacific Islanders
Total Enrolled	4	3	1	2

Principal Contacts:

Clyde B. Jensen, Ph.D., President
Harry P. Kornhiser, D.O., Academic Dean
Fredric W. Smith, Associate Dean for Students/Alumni

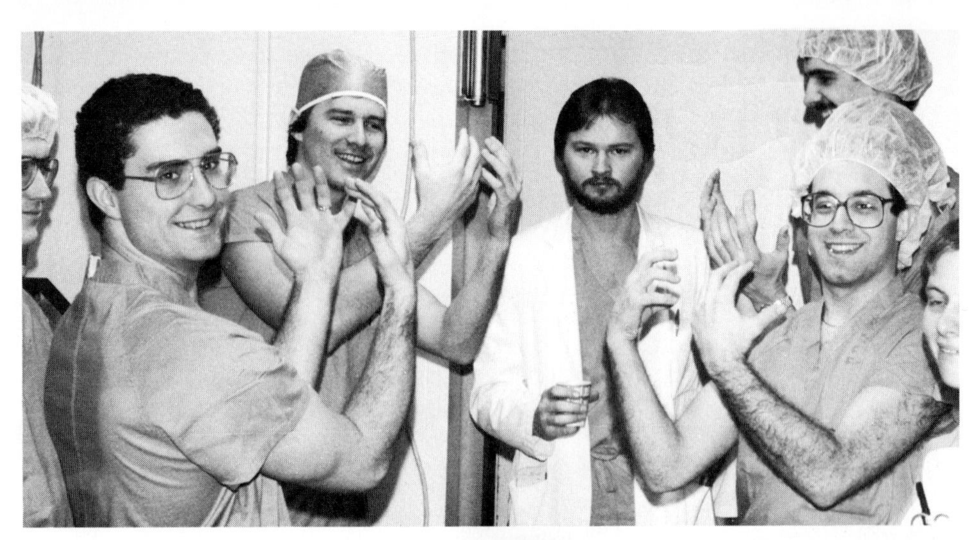

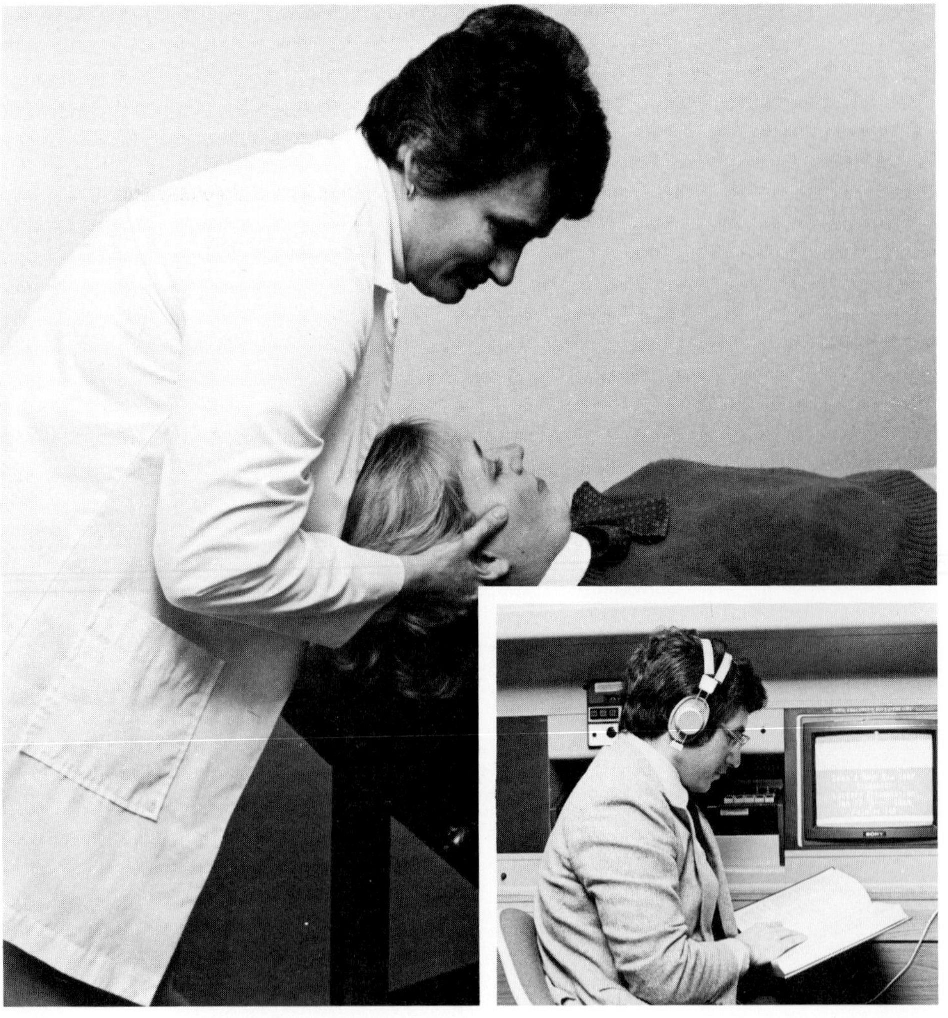

Information Sources

American Association of Colleges of Osteopathic Medicine
6110 Executive Boulevard, Suite 405
Rockville, Maryland 20852
(301) 468-0990

American Osteopathic Association
212 East Ohio Street
Chicago, Illinois 60611
(312) 280-5800

American Osteopathic Hospital Association
55 West Seegers Road
Arlington Heights, Illinois 60005
(312) 952-8900

National Board of Examiners for Osteopathic Physicians and Surgeons, Inc.
2474 Dempster Street, Suite 110
Des Plaines, Illinois 60016
(312) 635-9955

State Osteopathic Associations

Alabama Osteopathic Association
1511 North McKenzie Street
Foley, Alabama 36535

Arizona Osteopathic Medical Association
5057 East Thomas Road
Phoenix, Arizona 85018

Arkansas Osteopathic Medical Association
502 West 16th Street
Hope, Arkansas 71801

Osteopathic Physicians and Surgeons of California
921 Eleventh Street
Suite 120
Sacramento, California 95814

Colorado Society of Osteopathic Medicine
215 St. Paul Street
Suite 290
Denver, Colorado 80206

Connecticut Osteopathic Medical Society
Summit Farm
Joy Road, RFD 1
Woodstock, Connecticut 06281

Delaware State Osteopathic Medical Society
P.O. Box 845
Wilmington, Delaware 19899

Osteopathic Association of the District of Columbia
2804 Ellicott Street, N.W.
Washington, D.C. 20008

Florida Osteopathic Medical Association
2007 Apalachee Parkway
Tallahassee, Florida 32301

Georgia Osteopathic Medical Association
2157 Idlewood Road
Suite C
Tucker, Georgia 30084

Hawaii Association of Osteopathic Physicians and Surgeons
Kaneohe Emergency and Medical Center
P.O. Box M
Kaneohe, Hawaii 96744

Idaho Osteopathic Medical Association
522 West Main Street
Grangeville, Idaho 83530

Illinois Association of Osteopathic Physicians and Surgeons, Inc.
900 East Center Street
Ottawa, Illinois 61350

Indiana Association of Osteopathic Physicians and Surgeons
8900 Keystone Crossing
Suite 659
Indianapolis, Indiana 46240

Iowa Osteopathic Medical Association
508 Tenth Street
Suite 300
Des Moines, Iowa 50309

Kansas Association of Osteopathic Medicine
1325 S.W. Topeka Boulevard
Topeka, Kansas 66612

Kentucky Osteopathic Medical Association
208 Crossfield Drive
Versailles, Kentucky 40383

Louisiana Association of Osteopathic Physicians
333 St. Charles Avenue
Suite 412
New Orleans, Louisiana 70130

Maine Osteopathic Association
303 State Street
Augusta, Maine 04330

Maryland Osteopathic Association, Inc.
c/o Bill Mescow, D.O.
23 Haddington Road
Lutherville, Maryland 21093

Massachusetts Osteopathic Society, Inc.
P.O. Box 147
237 Main Street
Reading, Massachusetts 01867

Michigan Association of Osteopathic Physicians and Surgeons
33100 Freedom Road
Farmington, Michigan 48024

Association of Military Osteopathic Physicians and Surgeons
P.O. Box 273294
Boca Raton, Florida 33427-3294

Minnesota Osteopathic Medical Society
Hoffman Clinic
Hoffman, Minnesota 56339

Mississippi Osteopathic Medical Association
330 W. Broad Street
West Point, Mississippi 39773

Missouri Association of Osteopathic Physicians and Surgeons, Inc.
P.O. Box 748
1423 Randy Lane
Jefferson City, Missouri 65102

Montana Osteopathic Association
Box 1299
Malta, Montana 59538

Nebraska Association of Osteopathic Physicians and Surgeons
1210 13th Street
Aurora, Nebraska 68818

Nevada Osteopathic Medical Association
2300 S. Rancho Road
Las Vegas, Nevada 89102

New Hampshire Osteopathic Association, Inc.
35 High Street
Manchester, New Hampshire 03104

New Jersey Association of Osteopathic Physicians and Surgeons
1212 Stuyvesant Avenue
Trenton, New Jersey 08618

New Mexico Osteopathic Medical Association
P.O. Box 3096
Albuquerque, New Mexico 87110

New York State Osteopathic Medical Society, Inc.
1973 Morris Gate
Seaford, New York 11783

North Carolina Osteopathic Society, Inc.
Bermuda Run
Box 667
Advance, North Carolina 27006

North Dakota State Osteopathic Association
Box 516
Valley City, North Dakota 58072

Ohio Osteopathic Association
P.O. Box 8130
53 West Third Avenue
Columbus, Ohio 43201

Oklahoma Osteopathic Association
1310 Citizens Bank Tower
2200 Classen Boulevard
Oklahoma City, Oklahoma 73106

Osteopathic Physicians and Surgeons of Oregon, Inc.
9221 S.W. Barbur Boulevard
Suite 301
Portland, Oregon 97219

Pennsylvania Osteopathic Medical Association
1330 Eisenhower Boulevard
Harrisburg, Pennsylvania 17111

Rhode Island Society of Osteopathic Physicians and Surgeons
232 Norwood Avenue
Cranston, Rhode Island 02905

South Carolina Osteopathic Medical Association
615 Wesley Drive
Suite 105
Charleston, South Carolina 29407

South Dakota Society of Osteopathic Physicians and Surgeons
c/o MASSA Berry Clinic
Sturgis, South Dakota 57785

Tennessee Osteopathic Medical Association
P.O. Box 390
Pikeville, Tennessee 37367

Texas Osteopathic Medical Association
226 Bailey Avenue
Fort Worth, Texas 76107

Utah Osteopathic Medical Association
390 West 800 North
Suite 214
Orem, Utah 84057

Vermont State Association of Osteopathic Physicians and Surgeons, Inc.
c/o John M. Peterson, D.O.
28 School Street
Montpelier, Vermont 05602

Virginia Osteopathic Medical Association
L.B.&B. Building
Waynesboro, Virginia 22980

Washington Osteopathic Medical Association, Inc.
4210 S.W. Oregon Street
P.O. Box 16309
Seattle, Washington 98116

West Virginia Society of Osteopathic Medicine, Inc.
4850 Eoff Street
Benwood, West Virginia 26031

Wisconsin Association of Osteopathic Physicians and Surgeons
34615 Road E
Oconomowoc, Wisconsin 53066

Wyoming Association of Osteopathic Physicians and Surgeons
Box 1298
Worland, Wyoming 82401

Recognized Foreign Osteopathic Associations

British Columbia Osteopathic Association
461 Martin Street
Penticton, British Columbia V2A 5L1

Canadian Osteopathic Association
575 Waterloo Street
London, Ontario N6B 2R2

British Osteopathic Association
8-10 Boston Place
London, NW1 6QH, England

Publications Available From AACOM

The Education of the Osteopathic Physician — a newly revised comprehensive book which provides information essential to the health professions advisor and the prospective student of osteopathic medicine. Included is information on the educational process — medical school through internship and residency, licensure, practice options, and history and philosophy of osteopathic medicine. Admissions criteria and brief overviews of the fifteen osteopathic medical schools are also provided.

$6.00 per copy

AACOM Reports: The Osteopathic Education Monthly — a newsletter published ten times annually covering issues affecting the status and future of osteopathic medical education. **Reports** includes special feature articles, events at member colleges, calendar of events, and other regular features.

$25.00 per 10 issues

Osteopathic Medical Education — single copies of this brochure are available from AACOM free of charge. Multiple copies are available at $6.50 per 50 copies and $11.00 per 100.

Osteopathic Medical Education: A Handbook for Minority Applicants — Prepared by AACOM's Office of Special Opportunities, the handbook provides summary accounts of the osteopathic profession, pathways to osteopathic education, and the educational and training programs of the osteopathic colleges.

75¢ per copy
Bulk rates @ $6.50 per 25 copies, $25.00 per 100

College Information Booklet — contains information on the fifteen osteopathic colleges including a brief description of each college, admissions criteria, minimum entrance requirements, supplementary application materials required, an indication of class size or enrollment, application deadlines, and tuition.

$1.00 per copy
Bulk rates @ $12.50 per 25 copies, $37.00 per 100

A Guide to Sources of Financial Aid for Osteopathic Medical Students — a comprehensive listing of financial aid resources available to osteopathic medical students, including descriptions of each program and eligibility criteria.

$6.50 per copy

Application Packet — contains application for the centralized application service, procedures for applying, and college information.

No charge

AACOM Organizational Guide — contains information on the organizational structure of the Association, a list of members of its councils, sections, and committees, and a listing of administrative staff and faculty in the fifteen member colleges of osteopathic medicine.

$5.00 per copy

Study on Competency Based Objectives for Undergraduate Osteopathic Medical Education — contains information on the minimum clinical competencies expected of a newly graduated osteopathic physician, the component elements contributing to those competencies, and a timetable for the introduction and/or completion of these competencies. Competency objectives for the five core areas of osteopathic medical education — medicine, surgery, pediatrics, obstetrics/gynecology, and general and family practice — are identified.

$18.00 per copy

1985 Statistical Report — a compilation of information gathered primarily from the colleges of osteopathic medicine. The statistical data, which are presented in tables and charts with accompanying text, relate to the characteristics of applicants and matriculants in the osteopathic colleges, faculty, curriculum, sources of grants and loans, and distribution of revenues and expenditures.

$10.00 per copy (available October 1985)

The Debts of Osteopathic Students — a survey that examines indebtedness of osteopathic medical students at the fifteen osteopathic colleges. The situations, characteristics, and plans of students are compared at their entrance to osteopathic medical school and just prior to their graduation.

$6.50 per copy